THE POWER
OF MOBILITY

THE POWER
OF MOBILITY
How Your Business Can Compete and Win in the Next Technology Revolution

RUSSELL MCGUIRE

John Wiley & Sons, Inc.

Copyright © 2007 by Russell McGuire and Sprint Nextel Corp. All rights reserved.

Published by John Wiley & Sons, Inc., Hoboken, New Jersey.

Wiley Bicentennial Logo: Richard J. Pacifico.

Published simultaneously in Canada.

For general information on our other products and services, or technical support, please contact our Customer Care Department within the United States at 800-762-2974, outside the United States at 317-572-3993, or fax 317-572-4002.

Wiley also publishes its books in a variety of electronic formats. Some content that appears in print may not be available in electronic books.

For more information about Wiley products, visit our Web site at http://www.wiley.com.

Library of Congress Cataloging-in-Publication Data

McGuire, Russ, 1964–
    The power of mobility : how your business can compete and win in the next technology revolution / Russ McGuire.
        p. cm.
    Includes index.
    ISBN 978-0-470-17128-8 (cloth)
    ISBN 978-0-470-22776-3 (custom edition)
1. Business enterprises—Technological innovations. 2. Business enterprises—Computer networks–Management. 3. Mobile communication systems—Management. 4. Business planning. I. Title.
    HD45.M379 2007
    658. 8'72—dc22   2007018193

Printed in the United States of America

10 9 8 7 6 5 4 3 2 1

To Donna and Kevin
Thank you for your love,
support, and patience

The opinions expressed in this book are the author's and do not necessarily reflect the opinions of his employer.

Contents

Foreword

Anyone who has been involved with the infrastructure business in the telecommunications industry for the past decade will tell you it's been a tumultuous time. From the Gold Rush mentality of the early Internet era, to the near total drop-off in equipment and services sales in the post-Bubble age, to the much-consolidated, more-muted, big-company-focused present day, it's been a roller coaster ride for all involved.

As with any chaotic environment, everyone is trying to make sense of everything around them. Theories are suggested and rejected. Explanations are offered and dismissed. There's lots of FUD (fear, uncertainty, doubt) going around, and yet a few tenets rise to the top as being generally accepted and reliable.

Moore's Law was one of these early suggested hypotheses that gained strength with time and therefore proofpoints. Moore's Law explained the era of plummeting costs and bursting processing capabilities in the early days of computing. It provided an ability to cull from the rapidly changing technology landscape some stability of purpose, and allow for solid planning, expectations, and in some cases, hope.

Metcalfe's Law followed. Metcalfe's Law provided a solid extension of Moore's Law into the Age of the Internet. Building on the decades of experience with other networks, from railroads to telephones, Metcalfe's Law provided a basis to value and exploit the Internet and all the businesses and concepts derived from it. Metcalfe's Law paved the way for all sorts of corollaries, from those that claimed "First To Market" advantages in riding the Metcalfe curve, to those that pursued M&A to obtain multiples on the market valuations from the resulting high subscriber numbers. "The Network Effect" was born, and the industry had its next big layer of stability to anchor its development.

Then came wireless to mix everything up again. "The Law of Mobility" is what it's been called for the past few years, posited more as a hypothesis at first, gaining steam recently as more and more industry data support the core facets of the Law, and providing yet more ability to craft sense from the chaos that accompanies the wireless onslaught. We've gone from custom military-grade communications, to $3,000 "bricks" offered to the few, to clamshell innovations like Motorola's StarTec, through to TREOs, Blackberries and the iPhone. We've gone through hundreds of "A" and "B" carriers, through flaming Iridium satellites, through cellular carrier consolidation and logo changes on trucks (bye bye, McCaw, Bell Atlantic Mobile, Cingular ...) through GSM versus CDMA versus Wi-Fi versus lots of other technology battles. We're witnessing a total and fundamental paradigm shift from staid, anchored landline phones and computers, to totally untethered, anywhere-in-the-world instant communications. There's no torch passing here, but rather a whole new flame in a new generation that is growing up on "always on" connectivity, constant network presence, and immediate satisfaction. We're seeing total abandonment of prior decades-refined habits in favor of whole new approaches to not only technology and work . . . but life itself.

Computing. Internet. Wireless. These disruptive changes have forever changed our landscape like the railroads, airlines, and telephone before them. Wireless enables Mobility, Mobility changes all around us. Those who are true strategists in their firms have no choice but to quickly make sense of all this dramatic change and plot the best path through. For many, from the landline-focused telephone companies to the historically lagging Postal Service, this is the Perfect Storm of their time—a time where fundamental industry tenets, technological capabilities and user habits all change overnight.

Russ McGuire's *Power of Mobility* hits this new age face on. He explains, with almost matter-of-fact simplicity, what's going on, where it's going, and what you need to do to 1) not be blindsided and 2) leverage the opportunity to your benefit. The *Power of Mobility* prepares you, in a step-by-step fashion, to interpret the opportunity presented by mobility into your firm's environment. He provides a literal roadmap for strategic planning and execution. Where he can't give you the answer, he leads by example.

Underlying all of this, however, is that solid, basic, stable tenet of his day, the Law of Mobility. It's the foundation for understanding the biggest single impacting trend of this age. The Law of Mobility has eclipsed from being a mere thought, even a hypothesis, or nary even a generic Law. It's Russ' Law now, appropriately so.

Moore's Law. Metcalfe's Law. McGuire's Law. A new stability is upon us.

Danny Briere

CEO

TeleChoice, Inc.

Preface: Welcome to the Mobile World

We already live in a highly mobile world that would seem foreign to a visitor of even ten years ago. Nearly 80% of Americans above the age of five own a cell phone. Our telephones, and our telephone numbers, are no longer tethered to a geographic location. We can place and receive phone calls wherever we go. In fact, nearly 10% of American homes have "cut-the-cord" and no longer have wireline telephone service.

The mobile device we carry increasingly is more than just a telephone. Device convergence is no longer just a cool concept—it's an everyday reality for corporate executives and mobile moms alike.

The most visible example of device convergence is the camera phone. According to Strategy Analytics, 257 million mobile phones with digital cameras built in were sold in 2004 ("Taking Camera Phones into Digital Still Camera Territory: Megapixels, WLAN and Printers," Strategy Analytics report summary by Neil Mawston, April 11, 2005, www.strategyanalytics.net/default.aspx?mod= ReportAbstractViewer&a0=2354). That's four times as many camera phones as stand-alone digital cameras. Our theoretical visitor from the past would wonder whatever happened to the traditional film camera. Is this dramatic shift due to camera phones having surpassed the quality of photo taken by an old Kodak Instamatic? Nowhere close. Not yet. But because we always have our mobile device with us, the camera phone's value is defined by its mobility—by the increased opportunities we have to take pictures—to capture moments otherwise lost forever.

One of my first encounters with the mobile value of camera phones was at a Major League baseball game. In the middle of an inning, all of a sudden the three young ladies sitting in front of me raised their cell phones in the air. Finally, I realized that they were taking pictures of their favorite player walking by in front of us—photos that otherwise would never have been taken.

However, an even more significant example of convergence is e-mail. Virtually all camera phones are bundled with an e-mail service specifically designed for e-mailing those captured moments to friends and family. As an extension to the mobile value of the camera phone, multimedia e-mail adds convenience value of immediately being able to share pictures and being able to skip the tedious process of tethering a digital camera to a computer to upload pictures into e-mail.

Business e-mail users see significant value in converged device–based messaging itself. Research In Motion created tremendous momentum for mobile e-mail with its breakthrough Blackberry products. As leading messaging vendors like Microsoft focus on mobility, the integration of mobile e-mail into core business systems is also becoming much simpler.

As a real-world example of the value of mobile e-mail, I'm writing this commentary while attending a conference. The only device I chose to bring to this event is my converged mobile device. During breaks in the agenda, I've been able to check and send messages, enabling me to interactively resolve a number of critical issues back at the office. Without mobile e-mail, I would have been forced to bring a laptop and would need to find a network connection and boot my computer each time I wanted to check or send messages. The net result is that I likely would have been less well connected and would not have been able to quickly resolve my team's issues during these two days.

A third area where mobility has been built into products is in basic information delivery. Combining high-speed wireless data services with the basic Web browser built into a growing share of mobile devices enables replacing a broad range of content-rich products with simple access to that content over the network. Mobile-specific Web portals provide access to specific types of data in a format that works well on the small screen. For example, I used to take my two-inch-thick Bible to church every Sunday. Now, I simply take my converged mobile device. Through the portal at m.seek-first.com I can access six different translations of the Bible plus a variety of other related resources.

Immediate access to dynamic content takes built-in mobility to the next level of value. For example, Accuweather.com/pda remembers the most recent zip code I typed in and gives me an up-to-date forecast as well as any weather advisories.

A more impressive example of mobile access to dynamic content is the emerging field of mobile television. An article in the September 22, 2005, issue of the *Wall Street Journal* began with this observation: "Alan Foster learned about Hurricane Katrina's landfall while watching news channel MSNBC—on the small color screen of his Sprint cell phone, while waiting for his wife in a shopping mall near Los Angeles." The article went on to report, "In the week that followed, he kept tuning into his cellular TV whenever he was away from a TV set. At work, colleagues gathered around his cell phone to watch live television updates on the hurricane's devastating impact." The mobility of this small-screen TV created tremendous value for Mr. Foster as he sought to keep up to date on the unfolding story ("Now, the Very Small Screen," *Wall Street Journal*, September 22, 2005, p. B1).

The integration of information about the status of the mobile device with network-hosted content provides even another level of mobile value. Since 2000, virtually all cell phones manufactured for the United States have been able to identify their location to the network. This is generally for emergency location purposes (E911) and usually involves installing a global positioning system (GPS) chip inside the device. By linking my precise current location with centralized databases, applications such as Garmin Mobile's mapping and turn-by-turn directions services are made possible.

The consumer applications just noted are simple examples of mobility's being built into everyday products including cameras, e-mail, books, weather reports, televisions, and maps to create tremendous new value. The Age of Mobility is upon us. How will it impact you and your business in the months and years to come?

What's in this Book for You

This book introduces an observation as simple as Metcalfe's Law of Network Value, but relative to mobility. I believe that this observation, this Law of Mobility, should serve as a beacon announcing the emerging Age of Mobility and indicating how new value is created in this new age.

To save you from searching ahead, the Law of Mobility, simply stated, is that the value of any product or service increases with its mobility, where the value of mobility is realized as increased availability and contextual relevance.

As the title implies, this book will help you to capture the power of mobility in your business. The core of the book is a clear and implementable framework for capturing that power: the seven steps to the power of mobility. We will introduce the seven steps, then dive into each one to explain how to implement it to capture the power of mobility in your products, services, and processes.

To further solidify these seven steps, we will introduce case studies of companies that have already successfully implemented this framework in capturing the power of mobility and redefined the rules of competition in their industries.

This book's value should be measured by how well it helps you look forward, to envision the power of mobility in your business and to implement the steps required to turn vision into reality.

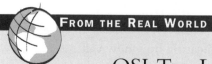

FROM THE REAL WORLD

OSI Ten-Layer Stack

Any communications technologist worth his salt will pepper his speech with oblique references to the OSI seven-layer stack (http://en.wikipedia.org/wiki/OSI_model). This very helpful model was codified by the International Organization for Standardization (OSI) in the 1970s and provides a framework for understanding how communications flow between systems across different networking technologies.

Throughout this book, I will refer to these seven layers, plus an additional three that I believe are necessary to complete the technology decision-making process, as shown in Exhibit 1.

The lowest layer (layer one or the physical layer) of the OSI stack represents the most basic physical levels of connectivity, such as how networking signals are sent across a piece of copper wire. The

EXHIBIT 1

The Pierce Ten-Layer Stack

Politics Layer
Finance Layer
Marketing Layer
Application Layer
Presentation Layer
Session Layer
Transport Layer
Network Layer
Data Link Layer
Physical Layer

FROM THE REAL WORLD (CONTINUED)

next level (layer two or data link layer) represents basic addressing and protocols for physical devices on a network. The most commonly known example of a layer 2 protocol is Ethernet. Layer three (the network layer) protocols deal with the basics of moving information across networks of physical connectivity. An example layer three protocol is Internet Protocol (IP). The transport layer (layer four) deals with network reliability. Transmission Control Protocol (TCP) is an example of a layer four protocol. And so on, up to layer seven, the application layer, which takes data transferred to and from the network and interprets that information for useful work.

Having spent 20 years in the technology industry, I am quite conversant in the seven-layer stack. However, Andrew Pierce, a friend who has spent his career helping companies actually choose and implement these technologies, taught me that it is the layers above the application layer that really matter when businesses are selecting technology solutions.

Andrew would argue for the addition of a layer eight (the marketing layer) that translates all the technical capabilities represented by layers one through seven into addressing real and perceived customer needs. If the technology doesn't solve a real problem, then it's not likely to be implemented.

Layer nine (the finance layer), he would attest, considers all of the costs of implementing the technology and balances those costs against the benefits promised by the solution. Vendor promises, heavily discounted by potential buyers, have to outweigh the cost and trouble of trying something new, or they'll never get approved.

The politics layer (layer ten), he would argue, is the most difficult to measure or predict. Who knows whom? How much clout can be brought to bear? And which parties gain and lose power through a technology decision often have the most significant impact of all in deciding whether a specific technology is deployed in a network.

Acknowledgments

Writing a book is a bigger, more complex project than I'd imagined. Without the help and support of many people, this book never could have been completed.

First let me thank my coworkers at Sprint Nextel: Mark Bonavia, Tim Donahue, Steve Funk, Walter Magiera, Bill Reed, Todd Reinglass, Charnsin Tulysathien, and Adrian Yeoh all stepped up at key times to keep the ball moving. Extra special thanks to Steve Signoff and Rebecca Sesler without whose encouragement and support this project never would have happened.

Special thanks and condolences to friends and family who have tolerated my mobility and technology babblings for years and still encouraged me to press on: Mark Volz, Andrew Pierce, Charles Mather, David Cordeiro, Howard Janzen, Mom and Dad, Mindy, Laurie, John, Bob, Ginny, Joe, Robert, Kathleen, and especially Donna and Kevin who have to put up with it every day.

Tim Burgard at John Wiley & Sons, and Susan Barry at the Barry-Swayne Literary Agency deserve special commendations for patiently educating me in all things publishing and believing in this project.

May all glory be to my God, who made all of this possible.

PART 1

The Mobility Age

CHAPTER 1

Technology Sets the Stage

The oft-repeated curse says "Those that ignore history are doomed to repeat it." I prefer the more positive twist: "If you want to know the future, understand how the past keeps repeating itself." Since this book is all about knowing the future, we will start by understanding how history continues to repeat itself. Time and time again, new technologies have been introduced and broadly adopted, resulting in dramatic impacts on society and the nature of business.

From a business perspective, a new technology can reduce a business's cost to produce a product or increase a product's value. In most cases, this improvement is relatively small but still worthwhile to the business.

Some new technologies introduce radical change to business. The reduction in cost or the increase in value may be an order of magnitude change—meaning that it is one-tenth the cost or ten times the value. These changes are so dramatic that they fundamentally change the nature of the business, the nature of the product, and the reasons why customers buy the product.

When this happens, the rules of competition change. And the new rules typically favor competitors with different strengths than the old leaders. Sometimes the old leaders can adapt and survive. Sometimes they can't.

Stories of businesses that have been crushed because they have failed to believe and have denied the changes brought by technologies in the past will likely be repeated. Now powerful companies will be crushed in the future when they disbelieve and deny the changes being wrought by emerging technologies. However, the stories of businesses that have believed in the coming changes and have turned change into value for customers, employees, and owners will also continue to be repeated.

The Gutenberg Press Unleashes Reformation and Renaissance

It is almost impossible to imagine a world without printing. In fact, arguably, all of the other technology advances we will consider would have been significantly hindered in their development if economical printing had never been developed.

And we must remember that the impact of Gutenberg's invention was purely economic. Prior to Gutenberg, there were printed documents—many made by hand (manuscripts), but printing presses were also cranking out documents by the mid-fifteenth century as well.

The innovation that Gutenberg introduced was threefold:

1. Alphabetic movable type.

2. Thicker ink that would stick to the press.

3. Perfection of the materials to be used in making the type.[1]

The result was a dramatic improvement in the cost and speed of printing. In fact, printing a book became the first assembly line process—mechanically combining replaceable parts to produce a complex end product—predating similar industrial processes by 300 years.[2] These advantages were quickly recognized by others, and lacking patent systems to protect the intellectual property (and slow its adoption), movable type printing spread rapidly.

Gutenberg began work on his first product, a beautiful Bible, in 1452. He first sold the product at the 1455 Frankfurt Book Fair, introducing his innovation to the world. Approximately 50 copies of that original Bible exist today.[3] By the early 1470s, the printing press had spread to the major trade centers in Germany; and by the early 1480s it had spread across western and central Europe.[4] Within 50 years, over 1,000 publishers had printed over a million books using Gutenberg's technology.[5]

Prior to Gutenberg's invention, there was little reason for literacy to broadly develop within society. Books were so rare and expensive that it was meaningless for the average citizen to bother learning how to read. As Walter J. Ong noted, "Many of the features we have taken for granted in thought and expression in literature, philosophy and science, and even in oral discourse among literates, are not directly native to human existence as such but have come into being because of the resources which the technology of writing makes available to human consciousness."[6]

As a simple example, Ong relates that, prior to printing, most people never knew in what calendar year they were born. With no newspapers or calendars to regularly remind them of the year, such a number would appear to have no relation to anything in "real life."

Robert Logan claims that the characteristics of Gutenberg's press enhanced and multiplied the prior impacts of the alphabet "unleashing a powerful new force that completely transformed Western civilization, leaving in its wake the Renaissance, the rise of science, the Reformation, individualism, democracy, nationalism, the systematic exploitation of technology, and the Industrial Revolution—in short, the modern world."[7]

Bacon's Law

There are two key questions we must wrestle with for each of the technologies we examine. Why was adoption so quick and why did the technology have such an impact on society and business? In most cases, we'll find that there is a simple observation, a simple truth that explains why adoption and impact were unstoppable.

In the case of the printing press, the simple observation was made in 1597 by Sir Francis Bacon in his *Religious Meditations, Of Heresies*.[8] The observation, which has become known as Bacon's Law, is that "knowledge is power."

The printing press enabled knowledge, which had been a virtual monopoly of the church and the universities, to be distributed. As Bacon observed, with the distribution of knowledge came the distribution of power. The powerless hungered for the freedom that came with the new flow of information, and, of course, those who had horded knowledge were threatened as their hold on power became challenged.

Given this true observation, once the printing press existed, nothing could hold it back and its impact on society and business was clearly dramatic.

The Steam Engine Powers the Industrial Age

The first practical steam engine was invented by Thomas Newcomen in 1712. Newcomen introduced four key innovations that made the steam engine a practical source of power:

1. Techniques for generating a vacuum.
2. The managed use of pressure.
3. Means for generating steam.
4. The piston and cylinder for capturing the mechanical power.

Newcomen built his first steam engine to operate a mine drainage pump near Dudley Castle in Staffordshire. However, it is not Thomas Newcomen who is best remembered as the inventor of the steam engine; instead, it is James Watt.

In 1764, Watt was asked to repair a Newcomen steam engine owned by the University of Glasgow. In working on it, he realized there were a number of ways in which the design could be improved. The most significant of these improvements was the use of a separate chamber for condensing the steam back to liquid at the end of each cycle. This allowed more of the energy in the main cylinder to be retained, greatly improving the overall efficiency of the engine.[9]

Watt built the first working model of his new design in May 1765, and in 1768 he applied for a patent on the invention. However, Watt did not have the capital required to build a manufacturing business around his invention, and therefore to meaningfully profit from it. He sought out investors and found them in John Roebuck and Matthew Boulton. To justify the large expense they would incur in establishing their business, the partners went to Parliament to get an extension to the normal patent to protect their intellectual property through 1800.[10]

The industrial factory predated Watt's steam engine. Water-powered factories were operational in England as early as 1721 (http://en.wikipedia.org/wiki/Industrial_revolution). But it was the steam engine that really accelerated the pace of change that became the Industrial Revolution. The first benefactor was coal mining. Pumps driven by steam engines enabled deeper and more productive coal seams to be mined, doubling British coal output between 1750 and 1800.

By 1800, cotton mills were the chief users as the steam engine provided reliable and continuous power for spinning. Up until 1750, agriculture had dominated the British economy. British agriculture was 2.5 times more productive than that of France, which itself was much more efficient than the rest of Europe. From 1750 on, three export sectors became increasingly important: coal, iron, and textiles. Cotton was insignificant as an export in 1750, but by 1810 had become 39 percent of exports by value.

In short, the steam engine radically changed the nature of business. But it also had a dramatic impact on all of society.

From 1750 to 1850 there were two dramatic shifts in the British population. The first was simple growth. Agriculture advances supported England's recovery from the Great Plague. In 1750, it is estimated that 5.8 million people lived in England.[11] By 1801, this increased to 8.3 million, and by 1851 it had nearly tripled to 16.92 million.[12]

The second shift was from country to town and to city. By 1801, about 30 percent of the mainland British lived in towns. By 1851, more than half the population lived in towns rather than in the country.[13]

London specifically reflected these shifts. In 1750, the population of London was about 700,000. By 1800, it had grown to over a million, and by 1850 it had more than doubled again to 2,362,000. London had rapidly shot past all the other cities in the world to become far and away the largest.[14]

These changes also dramatically changed the structure of society. In agricultural Britain prior to 1750, most of the farming land was owned by wealthy landowners who leased the land to tenant farmers. The farmers paid rent in the form of the goods they grew or produced. The economy was largely local, with specialized tradesmen making the nonagricultural goods needed by the community.[15]

The shift from an agricultural to an industrial economy created clear distinctions between work and home. Prior to the Industrial Revolution, most work was done in and around the home and often involved many members of the family. As work moved out of the home and into the factory, the men followed the work first, while the women stayed to care for the family and the home. However, in time, industrial productivity required even more workers, and women and then children were drawn into the workforce, creating tremendous social stress. The first child labor laws were passed in 1833 to bring the greatest dangers under control.

As referenced before, Watt's invention also sparked a new era of capitalism. The Industrial Age introduced business opportunities that required significant levels of funding. Notably, the London Stock

Exchange formally opened on March 3, 1801, reflecting this new era of capitalism.

The Second Law of Thermodynamics

As with the printing press, we must answer the questions of why the steam engine was rapidly adopted and why it had such an impact on business and society.

Bacon's Law observed the philosophical truths that answered these questions for the printing press. For the steam engine, the answer has a much more scientific foundation.

In 1865, Rudolf Clausius developed the classic statement that we know as the Second Law of Thermodynamics.[16] The statement is rather complex and is accurately quoted as "the entropy of an isolated system not at thermal equilibrium will tend to increase over time, approaching a maximum value." However, in practical terms this means that heat flows from hot places to cold places.

Big deal, right? Well, this simple truth that heat flows to where there isn't heat is what made the steam engine work and create motive power. The steam engine came onto the scene at the precise moment when mines and factories were ramping up their need for motive power. The dramatic increase in power produced by the steam engine then drove even greater productivity in industry, radically changing the shape of business and society.

The Telegraph Signals the Telecom Era

The telecommunications industry was born on March 2, 1791, in Brulon, France. On that day, brothers Claude and René Chappe demonstrated the first practical optical telegraph system. Claude Chappe wanted to call the invention the tachygraphe—meaning "fast writer"—but instead the name telegraphe—or "far writer"—stuck instead.[17]

However, it wasn't until electric telegraphy, whose invention is broadly attributed to Samuel Morse based on work he completed between 1832 and 1838, that practical telecommunications actually began to significantly impact the world. In 1843, Congress approved funds to build the first telegraph line in the United States from Washington to Baltimore, and on May 24 of that year, the famous "first message" of "What hath God wrought!" was transmitted over the line opening the American telecommunications industry.[18]

A new company, the Magnetic Telegraph Company, was formed and completed its first link, between New York and Philadelphia, in January 1846. Before this line opened, the only telegraph in the country was the original 40-mile stretch. By 1848, this had grown to approximately 2,000 miles, and by 1852 there were over 23,000 miles of telegraph lines in operation, with another 10,000 miles under construction.[19]

Writing in 1852, Laurence Turnbull noted that the growth in capacity and traffic showed "how important an agent the telegraph has become in the transmission of business communications. It is every day coming more into use, and every day adding to its power to be useful."

In 1861, the transcontinental telegraph line was completed to California. This new communications link made obsolete the Pony Express, enabling the instant communication of information that previously had taken 10 days. The Pony Express itself had dramatically improved the previous time of 20 days for a message to reach the West Coast.

International routes also began to be built. England and France were connected in 1851 and the first transatlantic cable was installed in 1858. Prior to these investments, international communications took as long as it took for ships to sail. A message from London to Bombay and back could take 10 weeks. But by the 1870s, a message from London to Bombay and back could take four minutes.[20]

The telegraph dramatically changed diplomacy, financial and commodities markets, and the news industry.

These changes in specific industries also had dramatic effects on all businesses. The telegraph effectively enabled the growth of very large businesses with centralized hierarchical command-and-control management styles. The increase in information flow also increased the pace of business decisions of all kinds and began the trend toward today's business pulse.

These changes, especially in the news industry, also dramatically changed how society looked at the world. Originally, all news was local. Local newspapers carried local news, and news only traveled to other places as the newspapers themselves were carried along. Timeliness of news was not a major focus, since it could be weeks or months before news reached distant corners of the country or world. As newspapers shifted to reporting on national and then global events, and as the news being reported increasingly was still happening (not an event already over), how people interacted with the news, and ultimately with the world, changed in the same ways as businesses. People became much more aware of places and events around them and the news of "now" really caught their attention.[21]

"Time Is Money"

Again, we must ask the question, "Why?" Why was the telegraph so rapidly adopted, and why did it have such an impact on business and society?

Writing in 1748, Ben Franklin made the truthful observation that answers our question and that should help us understand why any technology that helps us gain information and/or make a decision and/or complete a task more quickly will always be highly valued. He said, "Remember that time is money."

Businessmen using more recent information to outwit their competitors clearly learned how to use the telegraph to turn time into money. Newspapers could sell more copies of their paper with more timely news, proving that time is money.

The financial value created by telecommunications continues to this day, even as mobility enables information to reach us, and us to reach information whenever and wherever we go.

The Microprocessor Produces the Personal Computer (PC) Era

The ENIAC (Electronic Numerical Integrator and Calculator) is often credited as the first electronic computer. It was built in 1945 at the University of Pennsylvania under the direction of J. Presper Eckert and John Mauchly. The computer filled a 30-by-50-foot room, weighed 30 tons, and it took 150,000 watts of electricity to start it up. Instead of modern transistors, the ENIAC had 18,000 vacuum tubes and could store the equivalent of about 80 bytes of data.[22]

13

However, technically, the ENIAC was really only a big calculator. It could not store its own instructions. The first nonspecialized computer was the EDSAC (Electronic Delay Storage Automatic Calculator) built from 1947 to 1949 at Cambridge University in England under the direction of Maurice V. Wilkes. Although the machine included many concepts that we today consider standard for computers, few would confuse it with our modern products.[23]

No, the computer era, as we know it, had to wait for the invention of the transistor, followed by the integrated circuit, and finally the microprocessor.

While the Cambridge scientists were building the world's first computer, scientists at Bell Labs in Murray Hill, New Jersey, were inventing the transistor. During December 1947 and January 1948, William Shockley, Walter Brattain, and John Bardeen made the scientific breakthroughs that would be announced in June 1948 as the junction transistor. The transistor replaced the function of the energy-consuming, heat-producing, and failure-prone vacuum tubes in early computers with a tiny speck of semiconductive material.

A decade later, in 1958, Jack Kilby, working at Texas Instruments, and Robert Noyce, working separately at Fairchild Semiconductor, both figured out how to put multiple transistors and other components onto a single piece of silicon, giving birth to the Integrated Circuit and further miniaturizing the components of computers.[24]

Another decade later, Noyce was one of the founders of Intel. Through most of 1970, Intel's Ted Hoff worked to create an integrated circuit with all of the components for a complete computer on one slice of semiconductor. The first Intel "microprocessor" was delivered to Intel's customer, Busicom in February 1971,[25] and later that year Intel introduced its first microprocessor product, the 4004.

By 1977, Intel was selling microprocessors for $300 that Bob Noyce compared to the ENIAC in a *Scientific American* article: "It is twenty times faster, has a larger memory, is thousands of times more reliable, consumes the power of a lightbulb rather than that of a locomotive, occupies 1/30,000 the volume and costs 1/10,000 as much."[26]

In 1974, the 8080 became the brains behind the first personal computer product, a mail-order kit called the Altair.[27] This new class of computers inspired many new entrepreneurs, some of whom are still dominant players in the computer industry, including Steve Jobs, who founded Apple Computer in 1976, and Bill Gates, who founded Microsoft in 1975.[28]

Apple Computer was the company that really proved the concept of a mass market personal computer. Their Apple II computer, although crude by modern standards, was approachable and usable by everyday people. The company was started literally in a garage with $1,300. The real key to Apple's success was the availability of the VisiCalc spreadsheet software, which was initially available only on the Apple II. Thanks largely to VisiCalc, Apple's revenues grew from $800,000 in 1977 to $48 million in 1979.[29]

However, both the community of independent developers of software and hardware products for personal computers and the growing mass of computer users were desperate for a standard operating environment they could bet on. As businesses became increasingly interested in using personal computers to improve productivity, this need for a standard that would fit into a corporate environment became critical.

IBM stepped into this gap. In 1980, Bill Lowe, laboratory director of IBM's Entry Level Systems Unit in Boca Raton, Florida, sold IBM's senior leadership team on the vision of IBM bringing a personal computer product to market within a year. Upon gaining approval, Lowe handed the leadership of this Herculean task over to Don Estridge and a talented team, who achieved the nearly impossible. To meet the challenging timeline, the team had to work outside normal IBM operating principles, taking such innovative steps as introducing an architecture that was open to extension by non-IBM developers, using non-IBM parts and software (most notably Microsoft's operating system), and selling the product through non-IBM sales channels. Frank Cary, then IBM's chairman of the board, personally championed the personal computer effort and shielded it from IBM's otherwise smothering bureaucracy.

The resulting product, the IBM PC, was introduced on August 12, 1981 and was an immediate success. In the closing months of that year, IBM sold $43 million in PCs. By the end of 1984, the PC and related products were producing $4 billion in sales, enough to have ranked that division of IBM as number 74 in the Fortune 500 index if it had been a stand-alone company.

In time, IBM would stumble and be passed in PC leadership by more nimble startups, such as Compaq and Dell; however, the real winners were the people and businesses that adopted the PC. *Time* magazine recognized the impact of this product introduction, and for the first time in 55 years, instead of naming a "Man of the Year" or "Woman of the Year," they named the personal computer as the

"Machine of the Year." For the first few years of the 1980s, the PC market grew at 50% to 60% before leveling off to a respectable annualized growth of about 15% from 1985 on.

It is hard to imagine a world without the PC. Nearly every home in America has at least one computer, and virtually every professional uses a PC every day. So, the contrast with American business use of the personal computer less than 20 years ago is stark indeed. In 1980, fewer than 10% of small businesses in the United States were using personal computers, and within large corporations not even 3% of employees used personal computers on a regular basis.[30]

The PC and the software packages that made the computer useful were perhaps the first major example of a disruptive technology introduced from the home into the workplace. Before the PC, most technologies were first proven to be valuable at work, and then folks started using them at home. But not the PC.

Clearly, the PC unleashed tremendous power within corporations. Departments were able to make better decisions faster with fewer people. They could really get their hands on the data to run and rerun different scenarios to determine a range of possible outcomes and plan accordingly. Entire departments became obsolete overnight, including the word processing and data entry departments. And spending on big computers dropped precipitously.

But tremendous danger was also introduced. Many departments running their own analysis resulted in many, seemingly conflicting views of the "truth"—too much information became an impediment to decision making rather than an accelerator. Every white-collar worker became an untrained computer operator, searching frantically for the "Any" key. Critical data was lost when un–backed-up systems failed or critical data walked out the door on floppy disks as employees left to join the competitor. PC spending at first was out of control and literally uncontrollable since it was scattered across virtually every departmental cost center. Companies' centralized management information systems (MIS) departments were ill-prepared to deal with the tidal wave of support requests involving technologies they'd never been trained in.

"Moore's Law"

Why did the PC have such a sudden impact on business and society? The answer really comes down to the fundamental implications of Moore's Law.

The April 1965 edition of *Electronics* magazine included an article by Gordon Moore. At that time, Moore was at Fairchild Semiconductor, but later he would be one of the cofounders of Intel. Within the article were the basic points that later would be codified as Moore's Law—the observation that every year or so chip density (roughly equivalent to processing power) doubles while the price shrinks by half. Although the microprocessor wouldn't be invented until the next decade, Moore's Law became most meaningful in terms of the cost and availability of computing power.[31]

In 1965, there were very few computers and they could be used only to perform very valuable tasks. However, the continuous doubling of power and halving of costs meant that, by the early 1980s, it was economically viable for companies to move computing power out of the carefully managed data center and onto the desktops of average white-collar workers. The trend hasn't stopped, so today computing power exceeding that found in multimillion-dollar computers in the 1960s can now be included in cheap toys and everyday items.

The financial benefit of using this available power drove the rapid adoption of the PC by businesses and the embedding of computing power throughout society.

FROM THE REAL WORLD

Propaganda and Censorship

Throughout history, communications technologies have been powerfully used to bring about dramatic change in society.

As noted in this chapter, the Protestant Reformation is an excellent case in point—using the new power of the press to redraw the political boundaries across Europe, to reduce the power of the Church in society, and to encourage literacy and education. In today's terminology, we would probably call the reformers' use of rapid distribution of printed arguments "propaganda."

As can be expected, the Church in Rome (what today we call the Roman Catholic Church) was not pleased with the reformers' success in using the printing press as a tool to weaken their power. In fact, early in the history of the press, the Church attempted to gain control of the new technology, limiting the number of presses created and establishing editorial control over what would be produced. In 1487, Pope Innocent VIII commanded that all books had to be reviewed and approved by Church authorities before they could be printed.[32] Obviously, the rapid spread of printing and the relative ease with which new presses could be built, foiled those attempts at what we would today call "censorship."

Such uses and concerns over the power of communications technology did not begin with, nor have they ended with, the printing press. Going all the way back to the invention of writing, as great a thinker as Plato was philosophically opposed to the use of writing technology. Ong notes "one weakness in Plato's position was that, to make his objections effective, he put them into writing, just as one weakness in anti-print positions is that their proponents, to make their objections more effective, put the objections into print."[33]

Controlling the impact of writing eventually proved relatively effective due to the inefficiency of reproducing manuscripts. In fact, the Roman Catholic Church successfully censored books for centuries leading up to the Protestant Reformation, so the Church's expectation that it could continue was not baseless.

The real problem that the Church faced with the printing press was that the danger of the technology was recognized, and there were ineffective attempts made to manage that danger, but the power of the press was not recognized. Perhaps, if the Roman Church had been as aggressive as the reformers in capturing the power of the press, its ability to win the hearts and minds of European Christians would not have been so badly compromised.

Since the printing press, virtually every communications technology has been similarly used for propaganda purposes and has attempted to be censored. As I write this, the current debate centers on what some call "The Great Firewall of China." The government of the People's Republic of China recognizes both the power and the danger of today's equivalent of the printing press—the Internet. The government actively uses the Net to promote its positions while actively shutting down the use of the Internet—using technology and persecution—for promotion of opposing views.

Clearly, propaganda and censorship are powerful examples of the interaction of layer ten in the technology stack (politics) with all of the other attributes of new technologies. Politics and power can trump all of the financial, user benefit, and scientific arguments that can ever be made concerning the adoption of any technology.

Notes

1. Kreis, Steven. 2000. "The Printing Press," The History Guide: Lectures on Modern European Intellectual History. www.historyguide.org/intellect/press.html. Copyright © 2000 by Steven Kreis.

2. Ong, Walter J. 1982. *Orality & Literacy.* London and New York: Routledge, Copyright © 1982 by Walter J. Ong.

3. See note 1.

4. McNeil, Ian (ed.). 1990, 1996. *An Encyclopedia of the History of Technology.* London: Routledge.

5. Nesse, Randolph. 2000. "Printing," in John Brockman (ed.), *The Greatest Inventions of the Past 2,000 Years: Today's Leading Thinkers Choose the Creations that Shaped Our World.* New York: Simon & Schuster.

6. See note 2.

7. Logan, Robert K. 1986. *The Alphabet Effect: The Impact of the Phonetic Alphabet on the Development of Western Civilization.* New York: William Morrow.

8. www.quotationspage.com/quote/2060.htm.

9. See note 4.

10. "The Invention of the Steam Engine: The Life of James Watt." http://inventors.about.com/library/inventors/blwatts.htm. Extracts from John Lord, "Capital and Steam Power 1750–1800."

11. Langford, Paul. 1999. "The Eighteenth Century," in Kenneth O. Morgan (ed.), *The Oxford History of Britain.* Oxford: Oxford University Press.

12. Harvie, Christopher. 1999. "Revolution and the Rule of Law," in Kenneth O. Morgan (ed.), *The Oxford History of Britain*. Oxford: Oxford University Press.

13. Matthew, H. C. G. 1999. "The Liberal Age," in Kenneth O. Morgan (ed.), *The Oxford History of Britain*. Oxford: Oxford University Press.

14. Hitchcock, Tim, and Robert Shoemaker. 2003. "Gender in the Proceedings." Old Bailey Proceedings Online, www.oldbaileyonline.org (June 17).

15. Hooker, Richard. 1996. "World Civilizations." Copyright © 1996 by Richard Hooker. Washington State University, http://www.wsu.edu:8080/~dee/ENLIGHT/INDUSTRY.HTM.

16. http://en.wikipedia.org/wiki/History_of_thermodynamics#Entropy_and_the_second_law.

17. Standage, Tom. 1998. *The Victorian Internet*. New York: Walker Publishing Company, Inc.

18. Evans, Harold, Gail Buckland, and David Lefer. 2006. *They Made America: From the Steam Engine to the Search Engine*. Boston: Back Bay Books.

19. See note 17.

20. Ibid.

21. Ibid.

22. Gates, Bill. 1995. *The Road Ahead*. New York: Penguin Books.

23. Ifrah, Georges. 2001. *The Universal History of Computing*. New York: John Wiley & Sons.

24. See note 18.

25. Zygmont, Jeffrey. 2003. Microchip: An Idea, Its Genesis, and the Revolution It Created. Cambridge Mass.: Perseus Publishing.

26. See note 22.
27. See note 25.
28. Chposky, James, and Ted Leonsis. 1988. *Blue Magic: The People, Power and Politics Behind the IBM Personal Computer.* New York: Facts on File Publications.
29. Ibid.
30. Ibid.
31. See note 25.
32. "Teaching Gutenberg," www.hrc.utexas.edu/exhibitions/ education/modules/gutenberg/. Copyright © by the Harry Ransom Humanities Research Center, The University of Texas at Austin.
33. See note 2.

CHAPTER 2

Redefining Communications

This is a scary chapter. If you are old enough to remember what I am about to describe, you will probably nod your head as you read it and wonder at how much the world has changed. If you are too young to remember, you probably won't believe a word of it. But it's all true.

Redefining Business Communications

In one of my first jobs, to get to my desk, I had to walk past this open window in an interior wall. Sitting behind the window was a very friendly and helpful coworker. On a sign next to the window were the words "Word Processing."

After walking past this window and arriving at my desk, I would scan my desk for messages, quickly flip through the inbox tray, and flip on my VT220 text terminal with amber letters on a black background.

This was not that long ago. I'm describing the mid-1980s.

When I think of business communications in that pre-PC era, there are three artifacts that come to mind. The overhead projector, the pink message pad, and the routing slip.

Real-time communications meant one of two things: a face-to-face meeting or a telephone call. A "multi-media presentation" in a meeting meant transparency sheets displayed on a pull-down screen using an overhead projector. The transparencies were mostly black words and were probably typed up from handwritten notes by the word processing department.

Telephone calls were definitely constrained by time and place. My telephone number was tied to the telephone sitting on my desk, but also rang at my secretary's desk. If you called me, you hoped I would answer. If I didn't answer, you hoped my secretary would answer. If she answered, she would take down your message on a pink "While You Were Out" message pad. You hoped that what you said and what she wrote were reasonably close to each other.

At some point, my secretary would carry the stack of messages into my office and put them on my desk where I was sure to see them the next time I returned to my office, whether that be in five minutes or in two weeks. If you called after 5 P.M. and I wasn't at my desk, no one would answer and there was no way to leave a message.

Non-real-time communications meant sending something by the U.S. Postal Service. When your letter arrived at my company, the mail room would sort it for delivery to my desk. My secretary might save me a little work by opening your letter for me and placing it face up in my inbox so I (or anyone else wandering in my office) could easily grasp the content of your message.

If others in my company needed to see the information you sent me, I would staple a little slip of paper to the top of your letter with the names of the people who needed to see it. I would then put the letter in my outbox, and it would spend the next several weeks making its way from outbox to inbox of each of the people on the list.

And, yes, your letter was probably typed for you by someone in the word processing department. That person's initials would appear at the bottom of the letter to ensure they received "credit" for any mistakes that might have snuck in as they tried to interpret your handwriting.

The scenario I have described is not fiction. Isn't it amazing how far we've come in just over two decades?

So, what happened? The two main things that have already happened are the PC and the Internet, and what's happening now is mobility.

Moore's Law pointed to computing power being built into everything. Falling processing costs and falling storage costs led to a major shift from analog to digital.

The real-time meeting migrated to conference calls, video-conferences, and with the Internet to Web casts. Transparencies were replaced by PowerPoint. Voice mail became broadly adopted. Word processing departments were replaced by word processing software like Microsoft Word. Letters were delivered by fax and then by e-mail. Routing slips were replaced by the "Forward" button in e-mail.

Metcalfe's Law pointed toward a single network that would connect everyone—the Internet. Point-to-point communications broadened to multipoint communications. Connection-oriented technologies that required establishing a dedicated circuit were replaced by connectionless technologies that enabled different packets to be dynamically routed and multicast across the network.

Intranets replaced employee newsletters. Web sites replaced marketing brochures. Instant messaging (IM) replaced a walk down the hall. And Web logs (blogs) replaced heated debates in smoke-filled conference rooms.

The Law of Mobility points toward a shift from communications constrained by place and time to communications that are aligned with context and capability.

Already we see that the Internet, IM, Web logs, and e-mail have had mobility built in so that they are available to me all the time, wherever I go. Soon, these capabilities will be enhanced by new applications that respond to my context—where I am, what else I'm doing, who I'm with, and what resources I have at my command.

I cannot describe exactly what business communications will look like ten years from now, but I am confident that it will make today's IM and blogging seem as prehistoric as a word processing department.

Redefining Consumer Communications

It's not just at work that we've experienced revolutionary change in how we communicate.

In the mid-1980s, virtually all telephones were connected to the wall by a cord and many of them still had a dial instead of a keypad. Answering machines were an expensive luxury that few could afford, and even those models used cassette tapes that would rewind and fast forward to play the greeting then advance to a blank spot for the message.

Even if Caller ID had existed, telephones did not have a digital display to tell you who was calling, nor did they have built-in telephone directories, logs of calls from which you could redial, or a flash button for picking up another call, even if call waiting had been offered.

Writing Mom literally meant hand-writing a letter, and the flag on the side of that metal container outside your house was the only indication that "you've got mail." A message board was made with cork. A Tupperware party was the closest thing to a chat room.

Televisions didn't have computer chips, so remote controls were rare and primitive. Cable TV was a new phenomenon that hadn't yet made it to all of the suburbs. Satellites were what the Russians used to spy on us, not a great way to get television service.

As with business communications, the PC era signaled the shift from analog to digital and the Internet era signaled the shift from connection-oriented point-to-point to connectionless multipoint communications.

Mobility is already being built into much of how people communicate, so that, for example, a football fanatic who is an NFL Mobile subscriber can use her mobile device to watch football games, draft her fantasy football team, trash talk her competitors in online message boards, and send an instant message to her buddies to celebrate a touchdown—wherever she happens to be, whatever she happens to be doing.

Where historically, our location has largely defined how we communicate, as we move deeper into the Mobility Age, the richer concept of context is becoming the dynamic regulator of our communications. The meaning of this and its implications for our lives and our businesses deserve full exploration.

 **FROM THE REAL WORLD**

Business in the Pre-PC World

To get a sense of what the world looked like before the PC, Internet, and Mobility eras, consider these quotes taken from a speech by Paul H. Henson, Chairman of United Telecommunications, Inc. (the company that later would become Sprint Nextel) given November, 1979.

- "You all know, and probably utilize, the time-honored practice of dictation with a secretary typing the letter after it has been drafted a couple of times and you have done some editing."

- "You may not realize that only 28% of all business calls are completed to the intended person on the first attempt. . . . We could solve that problem by sending hard copy, instantly, to the desk of somebody you want to communicate with—after you've tried your call, of course. If you don't find your party in or available to talk, hit another button and have the hard copy transmitted. We're working on it!"

- "One wonders why in the world American business has tolerated this level of productivity in the white collar sector. . . . I suspect it's probably because some of those of us who call ourselves managers never thought it appropriate for us to learn how to use a typewriter or a cathode ray tube so that we could correct correspondence, speech drafts, and other hard copy material instead of asking secretaries or assistants to do so."

- "What will emerge is the so-called 'office of the future.' . . . It is going to revolutionize the way we do business, the way we communicate with our branch offices and our other business associates. We will be using a typewriter keyboard or reading information displayed on a cathode ray tube instead of dictating and typing those letters and mailing them out in neat little envelopes, wondering if they ever will be delivered!"

The revolution that Chairman Henson predicted is exactly what has happened over the past thirty years. Today, we can't imagine dictation or typewriters or even cathode ray tubes in our offices. We can't imagine "sending hardcopy" at a touch of a button as a futuristic concept that is hard to describe. We can't imagine a world without voice mail (a capability also enabled by computer technology). And yet, it was reality not too long ago.

CHAPTER 3

The Law of Mobility Signals Transformation

The Internet Connects the World

From the earliest days, the government, and especially the Defense Department was the biggest customer of the emerging computer industry. Much of this spending was done in university research labs.

In 1951, the Massachusetts Institute of Technology (MIT) founded Lincoln Labs, focused on air defense. The projects undertaken at Lincoln required collecting data from many sources, resulting in Lincoln becoming a hotbed for innovations in computer networking.

In the second half of 1957, the Soviet Union test-fired the first intercontinental ballistic missile and launched the Sputnik I artificial satellite, initiating the arms race and the space race. In January 1958, President Eisenhower established the Advanced Research Projects Agency (ARPA) to address these threats.

J. C. R. Licklider, a Lincoln veteran, became the first director of the Information Processing Techniques Office (IPTO) within ARPA. Early in 1963, Licklider proposed networking together the computers in research labs being funded by ARPA to make these expensive resources more available and productive. In 1966, Bob Taylor replaced Licklider as head of the IPTO and recruited Larry Roberts from Lincoln Labs to turn this concept into reality.

The network, dubbed ARPAnet by Roberts, ended up building upon advances in computer networking made by Roberts at MIT, Donald Davies and Roger Scantlebury of Britain's National Physical Laboratory, Paul Baran of the Rand Corporation, and Len Kleinrock of the University of California–Los Angeles (UCLA). These new technologies became known as packet switching. ARPA tried to get AT&T, the telecom industry leader, to participate in building ARPAnet. Bob Taylor recalls, "When I asked AT&T to participate in the ARPAnet, they assured me that packet switching wouldn't work."[1]

So the research community had to build it themselves. Boston firm, Bolt, Baraneck & Newman (BBN) was selected to build the critical piece of equipment, the Interface Message Processor (IMP) to link the computers together. The first IMP was installed at UCLA over the Labor Day weekend in 1969. The second was installed on October 1 at Stanford. The first message was sent between them and the ARPAnet, which would become the Internet, was born.

Initial growth came slowly. Four nodes were online by the end of 1969. By 1974 the network had only grown to 64 nodes, and by 1981 there were still only 213 nodes. In the 1980s, the network was roughly doubling every year, and the numbers finally started to reach significant proportions. By 1989, there were 150,000 nodes on the network. Between 1986 and 1989, the National Science Foundation slowly took over administration of the network, acknowledging the expansion of the value of the Internet beyond purely military purposes. Growth began to explode. By April 1993, there were nearly 1.5 million nodes on the Internet.

Applications also came slowly at first. Originally, the network was primarily used to log in to remote computers. In 1972, Ray Tomlinson of BBN sent the first e-mail across the ARPAnet. In 1989, Tim Berners-Lee of Switzerland's CERN started writing a program he called the World Wide Web. CERN published the program in 1991. In 1992, Congress passed a law allowing the use of the Internet for commercial purposes, unleashing an unprecedented wave of entrepreneurship.

The Internet burst into the consciousness of the general public in 1995. Most dramatically, Netscape's unbelievably rich initial public offering (IPO) of stock on August 9 captured everyone's attention and launched a thousand start-ups. However, other companies that would have a much more permanent impact on the Internet, the economy, and how we individually interact with the world were already on their way and celebrated significant milestones during the year. In March, Yahoo was incorporated, graduating from a hobby to a business.[2] Amazon's online store opened in July.[3] The first auction on eBay was launched on Labor Day.[4] So, in a short six months, three of the companies that have come to define the Internet experience came into being.

Over the coming years, the incredible power of networked computing to deliver to us dynamic content, enable us to buy and sell in new ways, and connect us more directly to our extended communities fundamentally changed how we live, how we interact with the world, and how we run our businesses.

"Metcalfe's Law"

Why did the Internet have such a broad and deep impact on the world? I believe Robert Metcalfe explains it perfectly in what has become known as Metcalfe's Law.

Bob Metcalfe is best known in technology circles as the inventor of Ethernet. As an early participant in the building and use of the Internet, Bob recognized the need for high-speed intermachine connections that responded well as traffic increased. From this recognition came the Ethernet protocol, and later Bob built a successful company, 3Com, around this expertise.

Bob didn't see growing traffic as a curse, but rather a blessing. Bob observed that the value of any network increases exponentially with the number of participants in the network, and this simple, but true observation has borne his name ever since.

What happened in 1995 is that the Internet reached a tipping point in the number of users. The value of the network outweighed the cost of connecting, so more people and businesses joined, further increasing the value. By the end of 1995, you couldn't afford to *not* be connected to the Internet, especially if you were a business.

Today, the Internet is fully integrated into our lives, our business processes, most services offered to customers, and a growing number of products.

Wireless Technologies Unleash the Power of Mobility

The wireless age can be traced back to 1888 when German physicist Heinrich Hertz demonstrated the transmission of an electrical signal through the air to a "receiver" on the other side of the room. Hertz built upon brushes with wireless signals made by Thomas Edison and James Clerk Maxwell, but wasn't able to carry these wireless signals forward into any practical applications.[5]

That task fell to a young Italian entrepreneur named Guglielmo Marconi. By 1897, Marconi had received the first ever patent for this new "radio" technology and was busy forming a company to commercialize the technology and its applications. On December 12, 1901, Marconi and his team managed to send a radio signal all the way across the Atlantic Ocean.[6]

By 1907, Marconi wireless telegraph rooms were installed on all the major transatlantic ocean liners. At first, these systems were intended as profitable ventures, with well-to-do passengers paying premium prices to send "Marconigrams" to their friends and business partners on both continents and to stay connected with the news and dealings during their journey.[7] However, with the sinking of the *Titanic* in April 1912, a new value of mobility was discovered. As the ship was going down, its Marconi operator stayed at his post frantically tapping out an SOS message with the ship's coordinates. The *Carpathia* heard the message and sailed 50 miles to save 700 passengers that otherwise would undoubtedly have perished.[8] Unfortunately, the *California*, a ship that was much closer and could have saved many more, failed to receive the signal because their Marconi operator had turned in for the night.[9] From that night on, the threefold value of wireless was clear: business, pleasure, and safety.

Wireless communications continued to develop slowly through most of the twentieth century. In 1921, the Detroit Police Department began using radio dispatching, but the system was transmit only. In 1933, the Bayonne, New Jersey, police department deployed the first two-way push-to-talk mobile radio system, filling each squad car's trunk with electronic equipment and requiring the officer to keep the car constantly running so the battery wouldn't be completely run down by the inefficient radio system.

During World War II, Motorola introduced the Handie-Talkie and the Walkie-Talkie, a backpack filled with glowing vacuum tubes and radio equipment to enable, for the first time, wireless battlefield communications.

In 1946, the Bell System began offering commercial wireless telephone service for the first time, starting in St. Louis and extending to 25 cities. The service used push-to-talk technology that an operator could then manually patch through to complete a telephone call. These systems used one set of channels to cover an entire city and surrounding area, significantly limiting the number of customers. Even as late as 1981, only 24 wireless phone users could be on the line at the same time in New York City and systems limitations kept the total number of customers down to 700. Obviously, something needed to change.[10]

That change involved both a new system architecture and new spectrum licensed from the government through the Federal Communications Commission (FCC). The new architecture was called "cellular" because it broke a city up into a number of "cells," each with its own radios, allowing channels to be reused many times over and greatly increasing the number of customers and calls that could be supported.

In 1981, the FCC announced it would offer two blocks of spectrum for this new cellular technology. The first would go to the local telephone company, most often the Bell System, but sometimes GTE or United Telephone or Centel or one of dozens of other small local telephone companies. The second was opened to new nonwireline companies. Starting in June 1982 with the 30 largest cities and working through December 1989 when the final rural licenses were issued, the FCC gave out a total of 1,468 cellular licenses covering every inch of the country.

A lot of wheeling and dealing happened over those seven and a half years largely shaping the initial cellular industry in the United States. The first surprising deal involved the Bell System. The breakup of the System was happening concurrent with the issuing of licenses. Since AT&T had performed a study that suggested the total market for cellular would only be 900,000 total U.S. subscribers by 2000, the company ceded its right to participate in the spectrum giveaway to the newly formed Regional Bell Operating Companies (RBOCs). The biggest wheeler-and-dealer among the nonwireline companies was Craig McCaw. McCaw started the 1980s as the owner of a small cable TV business in the state of Washington. By the time the cellular industry was fully formed, McCaw Cellular was the only truly nationwide wireless carrier.

The first wireless phones in no way resembled the convenient, attractive devices we carry today. At first, wireless phones were almost universally installed in cars. Later came "bag phones," which could be carried about but certainly couldn't fit in a purse or pocket. But that didn't stop folks from falling in love with mobility. By the end of 1985, there were 340,000 customers in 85 markets. Within two years, that number had more than tripled and the industry had generated more than a billion dollars in revenue. By the end of the decade, 5.3 million cell phones had been sold and annual revenues were at $3 billion. AT&T's study had missed the mark—badly.[11]

In 1994, AT&T finally got into the cellular game, buying McCaw for $12.6 billion and assuming nearly $5 billion in the company's debt. But the mid-1990s were also a period of technology advances that would further refine the industry. The first was leveraging Moore's Law to introduce digital technology into cellular systems, making them much more efficient and able to multiply the number of concurrent calls. The second was the emergence of a start-up called Fleet Call (later renamed Nextel) that used a new technology from Motorola to offer wireless telephone service using a previously inefficiently run block of spectrum called Specialized Mobile Radio (SMR). Due to its origins and regulations, the Fleet Call/Nextel service included a high performance push-to-talk capability that became wildly successful. The final new technology was called Personal Communications Systems (PCS) which would enable new data services. In July 1993, the FCC announced a new set of spectrum auctions to allow up to six new competitors to enter each market using PCS technology.[12]

One of the new nationwide carriers to emerge from the PCS license auctions was Sprint PCS. Today, in 2007, the U.S. mobile industry has consolidated down to four major nationwide players. The largest, AT&T (formerly Cingular), has been formed out of AT&T

Wireless (which started as McCaw Cellular) and three of the original RBOCs (BellSouth, Southwestern Bell, Ameritech) plus parts of a fourth RBOC (Pacific Telesis). The second largest is Verizon Wireless formed out of two of the original RBOCs (Bell Atlantic and NYNEX) plus GTE plus the most significant wireless parts of Pacific Telesis. The third largest is Sprint Nextel formed through the combination of those two mid-1990s entrants. The fourth is the U.S. arm of Germany's T-Mobile, largely formed through a rollup of PCS auction winners. So, roughly half the industry traces its roots back to the original license gifts to the big Bell wireline companies, while the other half has been formed out of scrappy upstarts that burst onto the scene in the mid-1990s.

One thing is clear—mobility has been a huge hit. According to the Cellular Telecommunications Industry Association (CTIA), in mid-2006 there were 219.4 million U.S. wireless subscribers, spending more than $10 billion per month for mobility.[13] And these customers have clearly begun to integrate their mobile devices into how they live, work, and play.

The global impact is even more dramatic. According to the International Telecommunications Union (ITU), it took 21 years for mobile technology to reach the first billion users worldwide. In comparison, it took 125 years for wireline telecom to reach that same billion. The second billion mobile users signed up in just three years. Wireline has yet to reach its second billion.[14] Philip Redman of research firm Gartner, Inc. estimates that nearly half of the world's population will be mobile users by 2010. Considering that up until now, less than 10% of the world's population has ever made a telephone call, the impact of mobility on how the world lives and communicates is huge.[15]

''The Law of Mobility''

Why has mobility so rapidly been adopted and begun to impact the world? In the fall of 2005, I made an observation as simple and intuitive as Moore's Law or Metcalfe's Law. Simply stated, the Law of Mobility observes that the value of any product or service increases with its mobility.[16]

This value of mobility is realized in two ways. First, and most obviously, making a product more mobile means that it's available for use more often. A product that is always with you and always fully functional (perhaps relying on a wireless connection) will be available for your use and translate into value much more often than a product that is usually left at home or at the office.

The classic example of this form of mobility value is the camera phone. Typically, a camera phone will not take as good pictures as a stand-alone digital camera. However, a camera phone is always with you since it's built into a product (your mobile phone) that most people take with them everywhere they go. Therefore, your camera phone is available to capture moments that otherwise would have been lost. Better yet, the camera phone also serves as a virtual photo printer since you can instantly use your phone's data connection to share the moment with any friends or family around the world.

The second way in which the value of mobility is realized is through increased contextual relevance. Mobility is the first class of technology that by definition regularly changes the conditions (e.g., location, environment) under which it is used. Since mobility is a highly personal technology, the situation (e.g., availability, with other people) of the person using it is also constantly changing. Products and services that have been mobilized have access to information about the conditions and the personal situation in which you are using them, and can use this information to be more useful and valuable given your immediate needs. The next chapter deals with this in much more detail, but consider the example of Internet search to get a sense of the value of contextual relevance.

Internet search engines, such as Google or Yahoo, do a great job of searching all the content on the Internet and ranking that information in a manner that best represents the needs of all people in all places at all times. Such tools are very valuable. All of the major search engines have created versions of their services that work well on mobile Web browsers, such as those found on cell phones. Because your cell phone is always with you, these mobile-Web-friendly versions have increased the value of each search engine by making the service available to you all the time, wherever you go.

But some search engines have gone a step further. They take into account the location from which the mobile searcher is doing their search. If they are searching for Chinese restaurants and they happen to be sitting at the corner of 119th and Antioch in Overland Park, Kansas, then a search engine that takes this context into account and brings to the top of the page the four or five Chinese restaurants within two miles of that intersection will be providing a much more relevant result and one that is dramatically higher value than one that uses the generic "all people, all places, all times" ranking algorithm. This is the value of mobility from contextual relevance.

As the cost of adding mobility (availability and context) into products continues to fall dramatically, the Law of Mobility would suggest the value of products and services would increase if mobility were built in. This potential transformation of the previously ordinary to the mobility-blessed will likely reshape our lives dramatically.

Those companies that figure out how to lead by building mobility into their products and services will redefine the rules of competition in their industries, increasing the odds they can win.

FROM THE REAL WORLD

The Beginnings of Mobility

In December 2006, the Sprint Nextel intranet featured a story recalling the launch of both Sprint PCS and Nextel networks ten years earlier. Here's the text from that story:

This holiday season, wireless consumers can download songs and videos to their phones or buy a loved one a device to keep them connected with voice and data faster than you can say "yippee-yi-yay."

But during a December just 10 years past, our employees were launching an entire industry from the ground up, one that fundamentally changed the way we communicate.

This week marks the 10-year anniversary of the launch of Sprint PCS wireless service in Fresno, Calif. Earlier that same year, Nextel refined its iDEN technology and prepared to expand to markets nationwide.

In those days, the wireless frontier was wide open and yet to be settled by nationwide carriers and hundreds of millions of customers. Employees who were there tell tales of a wild ride.

SPRINT PCS TAKES SHAPE

"I remember showing up my first day and asking the chief operating officer 'What do you want me to do?'" recalls **John Garcia**, president–Cable Joint Venture, who was then vice president–Marketing.

"He said, 'We need help with everything.' We had to hire people who could do many things in many areas. We were true entrepreneurs."

In the early '90s, Sprint formed a task force to explore wireless possibilities, and in 1994 partnered with cable companies TCI, Cox, and Comcast to pursue a wireless venture. When the Federal Communications Commission (FCC) opened auctions for wireless licenses in 1995, Sprint Spectrum—soon renamed Sprint PCS—snatched up enough spectrum for an impressive national footprint covering 190 million potential customers.

Naysayers said it couldn't be done: Launching a multi-billion-dollar start-up that would build a nationwide network from scratch, use unfamiliar Code Division Multiple Access (CDMA) technology and introduce what *The Wall Street Journal* referred to as "so-called" personal communication services (PCS) to the mass market in a mere 18 months.

To make it happen, Sprint began a frenzied hiring process of full-timers and contractors to staff the start-up and build the network. Leading technology vendors like Lucent and Nortel stepped up, supplying manpower, equipment, and even capital to help fulfill our vision. From a blank network slate at the outset of '96, the company put 1,300 cell sites and 45 switching centers in place by year-end.

Acquisitions Spur Nextel Growth

What began as a dispatch start-up Fleet Call in 1987 quickly became an industry force in the early 1990s, thanks to aggressive acquisitions, mergers and the purchase of Motorola's SMR licenses in the United States. But Nextel really took shape in 1995 with a billion-dollar investment. This led to its 1996 evolution from MIRS (MOTR Integrated Radio System) technology to iDEN (Integrated Dispatch Enhanced Network), which combined enhanced digital cellular, two-way radio, and text-numeric paging in one phone.

Larry Krevor, vice president-Government Affairs in Reston, Va., planted his roots in 1989 as an outside counsel before coming in-house in 1992. He recalls the early days of "frenetic" acquisitions, intensive regulatory efforts to gain FCC approval and the build-out of the iDEN network. Nextel employed 300 when he started; growing to 20,000 by 2005.

Nextel employees adopted a "get it done" attitude from the start and most wore many hats. Krevor realized this while helping to open the Washington office: He bought furniture, networked computers, even connected the phone system.

But his big challenge was writing the filings for FCC approval. "I wrote all of them and even got in a cab and delivered them sometimes," he says, noting that Government Affairs staffs about 100 people today. "We were the underdog who fought enormous odds and had great success."

What we now know as iDEN came into being during the 1996 Summer Olympics, with a Nextel national network rollout beginning in January 1997.

HALLWAYS AND ... HELLO?

A nimble staff meant decisions were made on the fly and impromptu "hallway" meetings frequent. A few pizzas could once feed the entire crew, and one conference room sufficed for All-Hands meetings. As Sprint PCS staffed up, leaders routinely dealt praise, worked in the trenches and did anything to keep employee motivation high.

"We once had an All-Hands meeting where our general counsel turned up in a Roman centurion costume to mimic our ad campaign," recalls **Lisa-Anne Uhrmacher**, manager-Partner Development & Product Innovation in Overland Park, Kan. "He came screaming into the room with his costume flapping, bare legs glaring, while a propane torch burned in his hand."

Wireless was still in its infancy, so many employees learned by doing. **Leighton Tong** worked with Engineering & Operations technicians to build the Fresno switch and prepare for launch. The team spent long hours testing and optimizing the new network and were "on pins and needles" come launch day.

"We had the launch event with media, city dignitaries, and Sprint executives in a building that was half underground. We worried whether the signal would penetrate it," says Tong, RF Engineer-Lower Valley Design in Fresno. "When that first call went through OK, we all took a collective breath and cheered, 'It worked—we're part of history!' "

Gene Guevel, manager–SCS Customer Care Technology in Overland Park, experienced similar butterflies preparing to launch the first Customer Care Center in Fort Worth, Texas. He and other managers recruited, staffed, and trained 800 specialists for the 150,000-square-foot facility. Imagine their surprise when the first customer call came in the Monday before Thanksgiving in 1996 and the specialist flubbed, "Hello?"

"We were expecting, 'Thank you for calling Sprint PCS. How may I help you?' After some fast scripting and training, we were soon activating customers very quickly," Guevel says.

FROM BAGS TO BRICKS

Back then, cellular was a rare commodity—bulky bag phones were the only option and calls could cost $1/minute. **Ray Kaufman**, accounting manager-IT in Lone Tree, Colo., remembers Nextel's original bag phone: "It weighed about eight pounds and looked like a gym bag." Staffers were delighted when the smaller "brick"—the Lingo—debuted, weighing "about three pounds."

Kaufman joined Nextel in 1994 to help set up its billing, collections and fraud systems in the Denver market. He remembers his first day, finding the conference room the only "furnished" office—with a folding table and chairs. The supply closet was equally sparse, offering blue graph paper and red pencils.

His most memorable near-crisis was the night before a big billing system conversion. During testing, his group realized they'd accidentally deleted files with customers' names and addresses. A dozen dedicated employees stayed until 4 A.M., reentering data to ensure a successful launch later that morning. "It was quite a fun time. You felt like you really made a difference with everything you touched," Kaufman recalls.

When new salespeople fret and complain about selling in today's competitive market, **James "JR" Roberts**, senior indirect account executive, Indirect Sales, Philadelphia, chuckles and reminds them about the challenges he faced when he joined Nextel's Philadelphia market in 1995. He had three products to sell, each of which cost about $1,100 and presented a downside:

- The Lingo ("A hand-held unit that doubled as a hammer. When worn on a belt, the antenna tickled your armpit.")
- The iM 370 PowerFone for your car ("Your car was out of service for up to two days while it was being installed.")
- A base station ("This was just the iM 370 with a power supply. 'You don't mind if we drill a hole in your roof for the antenna, do you?'")

Add to this two rate plan choices and coverage stemming from the market's five towers, which only provided about 20- to 30-mile coverage.

BLAZING TRAILS TOMORROW

Doing what it takes to simplify the business. Dedicating ourselves to customers. Innovating with technology to offer customers services they haven't yet dreamed of.

Notes

1. Segaller, Stephen. 1998. *Nerds 2.0.1: A Brief History of the Internet.* New York: TV Books, LLC. Copyright © 1998 by Oregon Public Broadcasting.

2. http://yahoo.client.shareholder.com/press/timeline.cfm.

3. http://phx.corporate-ir.net/phoenix.zhtml?c=97664&p=irol faq#6986.

4. http://investor.ebay.com/faq.cfm.

5. Newhouse, Elizabeth L. (ed.). 1988. *Inventors and Discoverers: Changing Our World*. Washington, D.C.: National Geographic Society.

6. Adler, Robert A. 2002. *Science Firsts: From the Creation of Science to the Science of Creation*. Hoboken, N.J.: John Wiley & Sons.

7. Murray, James B. Jr. 2001. *Wireless Nation: The Frenzied Launch of the Cellular Revolution in America*. Cambridge, Mass.: Perseus Publishing.

8. Ibid.

9. Masini, Giancarlo. 1976. *Marconi*. New York: Marsilio Publishers.

10. See note 7.

11. Ibid.

12. Ibid.

13. www.ctia.org/research_statistics/statistics/index.cfm/AID/10202.

14. www.itu.int/osg/spu/publications/digitalife/lifestylesdigital.html.

15. www.physorg.com/printnews.php?newsid=12090.

16. www.businessreform.com/article.php?articleID=11543.

CHAPTER 4

What Power?

This book is all about the power of mobility. Before we can get too far in capturing this power, we need to understand how the realities of mobility translate into power or value for your business.

For historical perspective, let's recall how the personal computer (PC) and the Internet created value. The PC provided local computing power and storage, enabling the user to rapidly adapt computer-based work to her changing needs. This was most evident with the introduction of VisiCalc, the first PC-based spreadsheet software. Using VisiCalc on a PC enabled the user to run and rerun multiple different scenarios quickly and efficiently without needing to schedule computer time. The PC price point enabled companies to buy PCs for a growing portion of their employee base to capture this power, making employees more productive and leading to quicker and better decisions.

The Internet provided network connections that crossed organizational boundaries. This enabled information to more easily flow, especially from trusted content providers. It enabled computer-based transactions to occur between companies and their customers (both business and consumer). And it enabled improved communications, facilitating stronger relationships and accelerated decisions. These value enablers are often referred to as the three Cs: content, commerce, and community.

When we talk about mobility, we see two additional Cs coming into play in creating power or value: context and convergence.

By definition, mobility means things move. The context in which products are used or services are offered changes in a mobilized world, much more so than in a premobility environment. By adapting to these contextual changes, mobilized products and services have the opportunity to be more relevant to the user, creating tremendous new power or value.

Convergence is a concept that describes things that used to be distinct and separate coming together to be one. In mobility, this is most often realized through device convergence, specifically with more and more products being built into the cell phone. This form of convergence creates value because that product (e.g., a camera) that used to be separate is now with you all the time, and because it is now always available, it is more valuable to you. However, there are other forms of convergence, including network convergence, which creates value through cost savings; application convergence, which creates value through integration that increases relevance and efficiency; and lifestyle convergence, which creates value through increased productivity.

Context Matters

Who are you? Where am I? What am I doing? Who am I with? What time is it? How powerful is my connection? Is my device's battery getting low? How busy is my schedule later today? How urgent is the topic?

All of these questions can influence how I want to communicate with you right now. Ever since AT&T patented Caller ID in 1986, we've been able to mentally evaluate many of the above questions as we see a call coming in. We can choose to take the call now or let it roll to voice mail.

However, even taking the personal evaluation approach is costly— our phone rings or vibrates consuming precious battery life, our mind is distracted from its current task to perform the complex evaluations in deciding what to do, and if we are meeting with someone else, that conversation is momentarily disrupted, sometimes changing the tone and effectiveness of the whole meeting.

What if our phone, or better yet, something inside the network, could take into account all of the contextual information and decide for us what to do with each call? How would that capability increase our productivity and effectiveness for the day?

One of the reasons that mobility's being built into every product and every process is now creating tremendous power is that all of the above contextual signals are being integrated into voice and data communications. Different applications can use different aspects of this context to appropriately take action. The voice call example is one that leverages all of the context signals, but others create even more value.

Who are you? How urgent is the topic?

As early as 1993, a telephone service called Wildfire introduced the concept of network intelligence to screen your calls. The Wildfire service provides a virtual assistant who identifies who is calling and either connects them through to you or takes a message. The action taken depends on how busy you have told the assistant you are, whether you're on another call, and whether the caller says it's urgent. Wildfire can even "whisper in your ear" while you're on another call to tell you about the incoming call and let you make the decision.

What time is it? What am I doing? How busy is my schedule later today?

Although Wildfire is still a pretty unique service, technology advances have enabled contextual communications to advance beyond what was possible in 1993. In 2003, a new company, IOTUM Corporation began offering a new service that "brings relevance to communications."

The IOTUM service takes into consideration time of day, what's on your calendar for now, what and who is on your calendar for later in the day, and your previous calling habits to determine how to handle a call.

The IOTUM solution uses a three-tier process to handle calls. First, the "contextualizer" uses standard protocols to reach into applications to check your calendar, your presence, and your connectivity. Second, the "rules analyzer" combines that context with what it knows about the caller and your past behavior to determine what to do with the call. Finally, the "services interface" completes the call, either to voice mail or to the telephone number that is right for you right now.

Who are you? Where am I?

Microsoft has taken integration with desktop applications even a step further with Microsoft Office Communicator. Communicator fully integrates with data in Microsoft Outlook, including address books and calendars, to fully identify someone, to know all the ways to connect them, and to determine everyone's availability involved in a "call."

Communicator also integrates with office telephone systems to make and receive calls, to establish conference calls, and to link incoming calls with the directory and presence information about them. Communicator can also direct calls to your mobile phone or other contact information stored in Outlook.

Where am I?

Moving beyond real-time voice communications, much attention lately has been focused on location-based services (LBSs). Since virtually all cell phones can now identify their location, that information can be put to productive use for business and personal applications.

On the consumer side, a high-profile application is child tracking, wherein parents can track where their child's cell phone currently is and where it's been. When Disney launched its mobile phone service, this type of functionality was central to what made a wireless service family friendly.

But there are other fascinating uses of location information emerging. Bones in Motion offers BiM Active, a program that uses LBS data from Sprint cell phones to record their fitness activities in real time, tracking distance, speed, location, elevation, and calories burned in outdoor activities. Kamida has introduced a service called Socialight, which allows people to leave "sticky shadows" as they move around. A sticky shadow might be a note or a photo that can be shared via cell phone with other people when they come to the same location. Users leaving sticky shadows can decide who else can see what they virtually leave behind.

Business applications may seem boring by comparison, but they are creating real business value. An example of the LBS capabilities being built for business applications is the Mobile Resource Manager product from Agilis Systems. This product includes five core modules: SmartLocate, SmartDispatch, SmartRoute, SmartCall, and Smart-Connect.

SmartLocate tracks the real-time location of an employee (based on the location of his or her cell phone). One application for SmartLocate is an automated clock-in/clock-out system based on when the employee arrives at and leaves a job site. Another is locating the employee who is closest to a customer in need. A third application is geofencing, wherein the employer is notified if any of his or her employees leave a predefined territory.

SmartRoute, SmartDispatch, and SmartCall all help improve efficiency of field personnel and improve communications with customers. These modules first generate work schedules for the day based on the employee's skills and inventory, and based on estimated drive times between locations. Throughout the day the schedule is adjusted based on actual progress, traffic delays, and the changing needs of the business (e.g., urgent customer calls). The customer is also kept updated on timing and status through SmartCall and can request rescheduling later in the day or on a different day, automatically adjusting the employee's schedule.

SmartConnect uses location information as part of an overall paperwork automation process to accelerate and simplify activities like time and expense reporting, work order updates, and inventory management. Using the context available, the employee has to input less information, and the business has more up-to-date, complete, and reliable information.

Of course, many more companies have introduced a wide variety of consumer and business location–based solutions, but these few examples clearly demonstrate how context is driving value as mobility gets built into every product and every process.

Converging Power

Convergence has been a buzzword in technology industries for at least 20 years. As PCs rapidly proliferated across businesses, many expected the PC and the telephone to converge into a single device. That clearly did not happen as a result of the PC revolution. On my desk, I still have two devices—a PC and a telephone.

Device Convergence

However, when I leave my desk, I carry with me a converged device that is both a PC and a telephone. My mobile device runs a Microsoft operating system and has within it a more powerful processor and more data storage than early PC pioneers could have imagined. My mobile device is also a highly functional telephone with features like Caller ID, call log, and built-in address book that similarly could not have been imagined in telephones 20 years ago.

But of course, device convergence has moved way past just combining a computer with a telephone. Each week at the law-of-mobility.com blog, I list the most recent announcements of convergence of products with the mobile phone. Every week, the list gets longer. For example, here's the listing from the most recent week's worth of announcements as I write this:

- Cell phone as (relatively) cheap gas finder
- Cell phone as traffic avoidance navigator
- Cell phone as parking spot finder
- Cell phone as sports radio
- Cell phone as TV remote control
- Cell phone as contraband
- Cell phone as newspaper
- Cell phone as steamy romance novel
- Cell phone as matchmaker
- Cell phone as diet aid
- Cell phone as watch
- Cell phone as blogging tool
- Cell phone as global Voice-over Internet Protocol (VoIP) phone
- Cell phone as international VoIP phone
- Cell phone as music player

Clearly, some of the items listed are more "feature" than "product," but the industry that is forming around mobility (some combination of media, content, communications, and electronics) clearly senses the value of device convergence as the most obvious application of the Law of Mobility—increasing product value by building mobility into the product.

But convergence is even more than just device convergence. At Sprint, we speak of four dimensions of convergence:

- Device convergence
- Network convergence
- Application convergence
- Lifestyle convergence

Network Convergence

Network convergence is all about making irrelevant the historical differences between distinct legacy networks.

Historically, at least in the United States, ever since the break-up of the original Bell System, there have been separate networks for local and long-distance telephone calls. These networks were interconnected, but operated separately with separate offers from different companies for local and long-distance services. Industry deregulation and consolidation have made those distinctions meaningless as providers combine local and long-distance into one all-distance service. Some of these companies own all the local and long-distance assets and some don't, but it's all irrelevant to the end customer.

Consumers and businesses have also historically recognized clear distinctions between wireline and wireless networks. Typically, they had wireline voice services from one provider and wireless voice services from a second provider, with very different feature sets, pricing structures, and value propositions. They also typically had wireline data services but did not have meaningful choices for wireless data. Today, all of that is changing. Consumers, and increasingly businesses, perceive that their mobile phone provides everything they need to replace their wireline phone. New high-speed wireless data offers are providing all of the speed and capability of most wireline data services, but with the increased value of mobility built in. The distinctions between wireless and wireline are becoming irrelevant, allowing customers to simplify down to one or the other.

Application Convergence

Another historical distinction has been between voice, data, and video networks. Typically, businesses and consumers had different wires carrying these different types of traffic, often with services provided by different carriers. Technology advances driven by the Internet era have enabled voice, data, and video services to all be carried by Internet Protocol (IP) networks, and the top service providers have focused on offering bundled solutions making the distinctions irrelevant to their customers.

Lifestyle Convergence

Finally, all of these advances enable the distinctions between different parts of our lives to be blurred, hopefully for the better—recapturing the ten-minute halftime during my son's soccer game to check my work e-mail and respond to an urgent request, using the five minutes waiting for everyone to join a midday conference call to research Mother's Day gifts, sending my sister a scenic picture from my camera phone taken from the conference room window while on a business trip. All of these represent lifestyle convergence. As one executive put it, "I used to have home and work. Now I just have life."

These four dimensions of convergence are significant proof points that mobility is happening and that it is creating real and measurable value.

FROM THE REAL WORLD

A Cautionary Tale

In 1994, I was head of new product development for a telecom carrier. During that year, our company entered into an agreement to merge with another in our industry. In December 1994, my team reviewed our current projects with the soon-to-be chief executive officer (CEO) of the combined company. About half of our developments centered on the Internet. My future top boss ordered us to shut them all down. His words still echo in my mind: "The Internet's a toy. Businesses will never pay for it."

I recount this story not to paint this man as a fool. In fact, within a few years he would become the most powerful player in the industry, defining the course his peers would try to follow.

No, I tell this story as a cautionary tale. It was perfectly credible for a powerful technology executive to believe in December 1994, that the Internet would never be adopted for real business use. However, within 12 months, this view would be proven completely incredible.

A decade later, I fear many business leaders risk making the same mistake in their assessment of the impact of mobility on business. Many see today's mobile applications and perceive that mobility may change how consumers are informed and entertained, but fail to see how the power of mobility can transform how their business operates.

Even worse, many will fail to prepare for the danger of mobility. By doing so, they will expose their businesses to tremendous risk. Businesses will fail and fortunes will be destroyed because smart people fail to pay attention to the leading indicators that are signaling the most significant change in how businesses operate in over a decade.

By 1994, the core technologies underlying the Internet were a quarter of a century old. Sure, improvements had crept up the venerable OSI stack (see Exhibit 4.1) from the move to fiber optics in the bottom physical layer to the introduction of the Mosaic Web browser in the top application layer. Those improvements mattered, but what really drove the explosive, chain-reaction impact of the Internet was beyond the OSI's seven layers. And it shouldn't have been a surprise to anyone.

Years earlier, Robert Metcalfe, whose layer 2 innovations in inventing Ethernet have had a tremendous impact on corporate networks, observed a reality in financial, not technical terms. Bob's observation, forever captured as Metcalfe's Law of Network Value, was that as more people used networks, their value increased exponentially.

The "so what" of Metcalfe's Law relative to 1994 was that the number of Internet users had been roughly doubling every year, but was still small enough to be below most companies' radar screens. Metcalfe's Law predicted that there was a tangible threshold of users at which point the value of the Internet would exceed the cost and trouble of connecting to it. That threshold was reached in the first half of 1995, resulting in new users flocking to the Net, further increasing the value, sparking the chain reaction that led to virtually every business wanting to be connected within a matter of months.

By failing to recognize the power that would be unleashed, as predicted by Metcalfe's Law, in the form of the value of dynamic content, electronic commerce, and virtual communities, that telecom CEO failed in 1994 to value the opportunity that was before him.

As we now look forward to how mobility will unleash new power through contextual relevance and convergence, are we properly valuing the opportunities we have before us?

EXHIBIT 4-1

OSI Reference Model

Application Layer
Presentation Layer
Session Layer
Transport Layer
Network Layer
Data Link Layer
Physical Layer

Seven Steps to the Power of Mobility

EXHIBIT 5.1

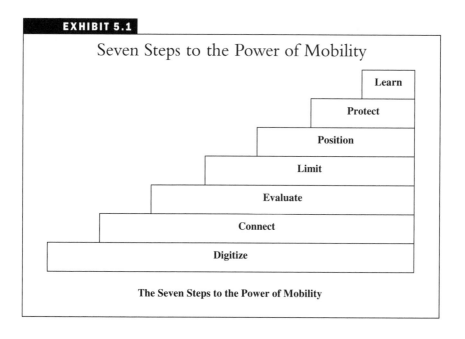

Seven Steps to the Power of Mobility

Learn

Protect

Position

Limit

Evaluate

Connect

Digitize

The Seven Steps to the Power of Mobility

CHAPTER 5

Introducing the Seven Steps

The Mobility Age represents an opportunity for businesses large and small to capture the power of mobility in order to create competitive differentiation and to take market share.

Large corporations and entrepreneurial start-ups alike should examine every aspect of their product or service for ways to increase value by taking things that have always been assumed to be fixed and making them mobile. Similarly, every internal process should be examined to identify ways that mobility can be introduced to increase productivity and efficiency, improving business performance.

Making a Product Mobile

In 1979, Sony introduced mobility into the world of consumer electronics.[1] The Walkman combined a small, battery-powered cassette tape player with lightweight headphones to create a personal music device that you could take with you wherever you went. Before the Walkman, people could listen to music in their homes or in their cars. Portable "boomboxes" had begun to be produced, but were intrusive, being too large and heavy for many activities and forcing the owners' listening preferences on everyone in the immediate vicinity.

The mid-1970s had been hard on Sony, as competitors like RCA, Zenith, Toshiba, and JVC adopted and improved upon technologies Sony had invented. The company lost share in critical markets and overall revenue growth slowed from 166% for the first four years of the decade to 35% for the next four.[2]

The Walkman ushered in the 1980s as a period of unprecedented growth for Sony. The company's sales and operating revenues grew from 643 billion yen in 1979 to nearly 3 trillion yen in 1989.[3] The Walkman also played a pivotal role in establishing Sony as a global brand standing for innovation and entertainment.

However, this success was not guaranteed when the product was envisioned by Sony's founder and honorary chairman, Masaru Ibuku. To keep dimensions small and the price relatively affordable, the Walkman lacked a record function. Critics claimed that no one would buy a tape machine that couldn't record. Industry experts could not yet envision that the value of mobility would outweigh any feature limitations in the product.

The Walkman truly revolutionized the electronics industry. To properly introduce the impact of the innovation, Sony held a launch event for journalists where the message was completely communicated via Walkman. The guests were ushered onto a tour bus where each was given one of the new products. The tape inside introduced the Walkman. The bus took the journalists to a nearby park where active people used the product while riding a bike and roller-skating—all choreographed to the taped explanation of the power of mobility unleashed by this radical new invention.[4]

In the first month of availability, only 3,000 of the initial production run of 30,000 units sold, seemingly validating the predictions of the skeptics. However, in the next month, the entire first batch sold out. Mobile music had become a phenomenon across Japan. Sony and its retail partners struggled to keep up with demand. Soon, fans around the world were begging Sony to take the product global.[5]

By 1986, the Walkman had become so ubiquitous and synonymous with mobile music that the word "Walkman" was added to the *Oxford English Dictionary*. More than 50 million units of the product family shipped in the first ten years, with that number doubling again by 1992.[6]

Not only was the Walkman a huge commercial success that helped put Sony on the map as a consumer electronics and entertainment powerhouse, but it also radically transformed how people listen to music.

What Sony did was take a product that, by assumption, was fixed and made it mobile. This transformation created tremendous new value for the customer. Music could now be enjoyed anywhere, anytime. Instead of being limited to the waking times spent at home or in the car, customers were listening while traveling, while playing and exercising, while commuting on public transport, and in previously musically deprived parts of their homes.

That value creation translated into growth for the consumer electronics industry, and most importantly for Sony, a strong foundation for the company's development into a global powerhouse.

Adding Mobility into Products Today

Just as Sony leveraged Moore's Law by using transistors and integrated circuits to make a small affordable tape player to revolutionize the music industry, Apple has leveraged both Moore's Law and Metcalfe's Law by applying the shrinking cost and size of data storage and accelerating network connectivity to once again redefine how people interact with the music that defines their lives.

Apple's iPod has accomplished for Apple virtually the same benefits that the Walkman accomplished for Sony, reversing a multi-year slide and establishing the company as a global brand standing for innovation and entertainment. The resulting halo effect has improved performance for the company's core computer products.

For the first six months of 2006, Apple's net revenues increased 50% over the same period the year before. Computer sales increased 6%, and software sales increased 44%, but the real growth came in iPods and other music-related sales. Music player sales more than doubled, and revenues from Apple's iTunes music service and related offers increased by nearly 150%. Most tellingly, music now accounts for more than half of the company's total revenues.

Both Sony and Apple are also participating in mobilizing other product categories.

In 2003, Sony announced the introduction of the Play Station Portable (PSP). Although clearly not the first mobile video gaming system, the product extends the company's leadership in innovation and mobility. Sony sold over 6 million PSP units in the first full year of availability.[7] Across the video gaming industry, mobility is driving growth, with mobile system sales increasing 96% from 2004 to 2005.[8]

Meanwhile, Apple is pioneering building mobility into television. In October 2005, Apple introduced a video-capable iPod and a groundbreaking agreement with ABC to sell popular television shows through Apple's iTunes online store. The company has since added content from other broadcast and cable networks. By midyear 2006, iTunes featured more than 9,000 video products and had sold more than 30 million video downloads.[9]

The television industry faces threats to conventional revenue streams, largely due to the growing adoption of digital video recorders (such as TiVo) which enable instant skipping of commercials. With the video iPod, Apple has introduced a new model for watching television that is delivering the value of mobility for consumers, redefining the business model to provide customer control while ensuring revenue for the networks, and inserting the company into the transaction flow for yet another industry.

I Thought Cameras Already Were Mobile

Like music players, cameras have also gone through two rounds of redefinition around the concept of mobility. Film cameras fell prey to Moore's Law with the rapid adoption of digital cameras. Now, Metcalfe's Law has kicked in and consumers are buying four times as many camera phones as digital cameras.

Because of this shift, consumers are enjoying mobility-driven value as they use their camera phones to take everyday snapshots.

But wait—haven't cameras always been mobile?

Cameras have certainly been portable. But for most people, cameras have tended to stay in one fixed place. I keep mine (both my retired film camera and two generations of digital cameras) in a drawer in the kitchen. I always know exactly where they are, which usually isn't where I actually need them.

By converging a camera into a device (a cell phone) that people tend to have with them all the time, the camera's mobility has increased, creating tremendous value for consumers and incremental revenue for phone manufacturers and wireless carriers.

So, what does this mean for products that already seem to be mobile? Most products can be made even more valuable by increasing their mobility. If customers aren't already taking the product with them 100% of the time, then there's still more value that can be added by increasing the mobility. And no matter how much people are using a product, if there is information or content involved, leveraging computing power and networking can further add to the product value and likely shift the power in the industry.

Specific to the camera phone, making it easy for customers to take a picture and immediately send it to a friend has dramatically changed how people take and share photographs, while the buying shift from cameras to camera phones has turned companies like Nokia, Motorola, and Samsung into photography market share leaders.

Can Mobility Increase the Value of Your Product?

But what about you? Do you have a product that you think might be a candidate for mobilizing to create more value? How can you capture the power of mobility?

The next seven chapters will guide you through the process of capturing the power of mobility in your business. We have identified a seven-step process that can be applied to virtually any product, service, or process to best capture the power of mobility.

In your business, you may have already implemented some of these steps. Even so, now is a great time to revisit exactly how you have digitized or connected your business and ensure that you are truly prepared for moving forward into the Age of Mobility.

The seven steps to the power of mobility are:

1. **Digitize**. Capture the power unleashed by Moore's Law. Digitize your product and your business.

2. **Connect**. Capture the power unleashed by Metcalfe's Law and the Internet.

3. **Evaluate**. In what ways does your product create value? In what ways is that value limited due to lack of mobility? If you could build in mobility, how would that increase the value of your product?

4. **Limit**. In mobilizing your product, what are you going to leave out? What are you going to choose to *not* do?

5. **Position**. Select the target markets, customers, and applications that fit the new value creation and what you're leaving out of your product.

6. **Protect**. Manage the danger of mobility.

7. **Learn**. Watch how customers use your product and adapt to the new opportunities.

Consider Sony's Walkman and PSP, Apple's iPod and iTunes, and camera phones. Recognize how these mobilizations first captured the available power of Moore's Law and Metcalfe's Law as foundational to mobilization. Notice that the Walkman left out the record function, and early camera phones have limited picture resolution to provide reasonable performance over second-generation wireless networks. Consider how each of these companies positioned their products for the appropriate markets, and appreciate how they have expanded their vision as they have watched their customers do new things with their mobilized products—applications that the companies couldn't initially imagine.

In the coming chapters, we will help you walk through these same steps to capture the power of mobility for your products.

Making a Service Mobile

Perhaps you are in a services business. Does the Law of Mobility apply to your industry? Is there a way to capture the power of mobility in your business?

Of course there is. In the minds of your customers, their experience with your service *is* your product. Is there an opportunity to take an aspect of your service that has always been fixed and, by making it mobile, increase value for your customers?

Consider the pizza business. This favorite food of Americans originated in Naples, Italy, centuries ago. Italian immigrants brought their local specialty to American ethnic centers early in the twentieth century. But it wasn't until GIs returned from World War II with a craving for the tasty dish that pizzerias began popping up across the American landscape. These restaurants, of course, focused on the typical dining room experience.[10]

The company most clearly associated with mobilizing the pizza eating experience is Domino's Pizza. The company that would invent the cardboard pizza box and the belt-driven pizza oven had a legendary start in 1960 involving $50 cash and a used VW Beetle.[11] Today, the company is the second largest pizza chain in the world, with nearly $5 billion in annual revenues, delivering over a million pizzas a day.[12]

Domino's created a delivery-only business. They focused all of their products, processes, and systems on taking the sale, delivery, and consumption of the menu items from the fixed location of the restaurant to wherever the customers were—at their homes, at work, at parties, at the park having a picnic—anywhere, anytime. And Americans have loved the new freedom, contributing to the Italian specialty's becoming a nationwide favorite.

Of course, virtually all pizzerias and pizza chains have responded, similarly offering delivery service. But Domino's has maintained nearly a 20% share of the delivery market. Is it because they make great pizza? Apparently not. Of the 11 pizza chains with at least 50 customer ratings at RateItAll.com, Domino's scored ninth.[13]

No, Domino's success comes from delivering good enough pizza at an attractive price with the added value of mobility!

The company's focus on adding mobility into the pizza experience has resulted in corporate success, but it has also helped the entire industry grow. Since 1991, the share of the pizza industry that is delivered has grown from 26% to 35%.[14]

Pizza delivery has also changed the way Americans approach mealtime. A Roper study claims that 73% of Americans have no idea what they'll feed their family for dinner even at 4:30 on an average afternoon.[15] Pizza delivery has also become a critical component for casual gatherings of friends. More pizza is eaten on Super Bowl Sunday than any other day of the year.[16]

And all because an entrepreneur saw the opportunity to mobilize a service that everyone assumed was tied to a fixed location!

Adding Mobility into Services Today

In 1987, Avis became a pioneer in leveraging mobile technology to revolutionize an industry by taking a service process that had been fixed in a company location and taking it to where the customers were. In that year, the company introduced the Roaming Rapid Return, using a handheld terminal to bring the car return and checkout process carside.[17]

Prior to this innovation, a rental car customer had to write down her mileage, unload her belongings from the car, and then walk across the rental car lot to a hut housing the company's point-of-sale terminals. There, she would wait in line for her turn to hand over paper, the information from which would then be reentered into the terminal, payment made, and finally the customer could run to catch her flight.

Virtually all competitors have had to replicate Avis's mobilized service. Today, by the time the traveler has removed her bags from the trunk of the car, a service agent has arrived at the car, used a bar code scanner to identify the car and customer, entered the mileage into a handheld point-of-sale terminal, and often has the receipt printed and ready for the customer so she can head straight to her flight.

This approach obviously leverages Moore's Law and Metcalfe's Law along with wireless networks to create tremendous value for the customer.

Others are seeking to similarly deliver this value of mobility for their service customers in additional industries.

Dry Cleaning To-Your-Door is a nationwide franchise operation that does exactly what its name implies—taking the process of dropping off and picking up your dry cleaning to where you are instead of the company's fixed locations. The company has developed the processes and systems to enable franchisees to deliver a quality service at a competitive price. The value of mobility creates the differentiation to enable the business to rapidly grow.

Can Mobility Increase the Value of Your Service?

The seven steps to the power of mobility apply equally well for service businesses:

1. **Digitize**. Capture the power unleashed by Moore's Law. Digitize your service.

2. **Connect**. Capture the power unleashed by Metcalfe's Law and the Internet.

3. **Evaluate**. In what ways does your service create value? In what ways is that value limited due to lack of mobility? If you could untether where you provide service, how would that change the value?

4. **Limit**. In mobilizing your service, how will you define limits? Will you limit the geography in which you provide the service, or will you limit the specific services that you mobilize?

5. **Position**. Select the target markets, customers, and applications that fit the new value creation and the limits you're placing on your service.

6. Protect. Manage the danger of mobility.

7. Learn. Watch how customers use your service and adapt to the new opportunities.

Consider Domino's, Avis, and Dry Cleaning To-Your-Door. Recognize how these mobilizations first captured the power of service data and connectivity as foundational to mobilization. Notice that Domino's limited its menu, Avis limited its mobilization to its own return lot, and that Dry Cleaning To-Your-Door carefully selects the neighborhoods into which it expands. Consider how each of these companies positioned its products for the appropriate markets, and appreciate how they have expanded their vision as they have watched their customers ask for new value from their mobilized services—opportunities that the companies couldn't initially imagine.

In the coming chapters, we will help you walk through these same steps to capture the power of mobility for your services.

Making a Process Mobile

In any business, there likely are processes that are well suited to mobilization. Taking these processes out of a fixed location may not necessarily result in increased customer perception of value but can drive increased productivity and efficiency, improving your overall business performance.

In 2004, Sprint began a program known as the Sprint Powered Workplace. In this program, as real estate leases expire at branch locations across the company, the staff within those locations are evaluated. Approximately 40% of field staff typically qualify as "work anywhere" employees. For these employees, there's little value in tying them to a fixed location and instead there is tremendous value in empowering them to do their job anywhere.

Many of these anywhere workers are customer facing. They are most productive when they are interacting with various folks within customer organizations. However, the bulk of the tools they need to do their jobs are maintained in the fixed location of the branch office.

Sprint has taken a number of steps to free these resources from the fixed office. Work-anywhere employees are equipped with laptops with broadband wireless data cards, handheld smart phones, and broadband connections at home. Through these connections, they can now securely access the systems that previously had been accessible only from their office desktop. Sprint has also established a system so that any required documentation or collateral can be printed on demand at any of the hundreds of FedEx Kinko's Office and Print Centers across the country and around the globe.

Of course, when anywhere workers want to come into the office, shared offices are available, along with all the normal resources to provide a productive office environment. In addition to improving the productivity and job satisfaction of these employees, Sprint is also on track to reduce real estate costs by $50 million annually.[18]

Could your business benefit from those kinds of savings? Are there processes in your business that could be performed more productively or efficiently if they were no longer tied to a fixed location? Would the employees involved view this as a positive change, and if not, how critical is the current staff to company success?

The seven steps to the power of mobility are also relevant for mobilizing internal processes:

1. **Digitize**. Capture the power unleashed by Moore's Law. Digitize your processes and your business.

2. **Connect**. Capture the power unleashed by Metcalfe's Law and the Internet.

3. **Evaluate**. In what ways is your process constrained due to lack of mobility? If you could build in mobility, how would that change the effectiveness of the process?

4. **Limit**. Are there aspects of the process that must be limited as you mobilize?

5. **Position**. Select the target applications that fit how you've defined the mobilized process.

6. **Protect**. Manage the danger of mobility.

7. **Learn**. Watch how your mobilized process uncovers additional opportunities for value creation.

In the coming chapters, we will help you walk through these same steps to capture the Power of Mobility for your processes.

High Reward, High Risk

Capturing the power of mobility is a high-reward opportunity. If done right, you have the opportunity to redefine the rules of competition in your industry. You will create tremendous differentiation and advantage. Your competitors will be forced to follow your lead on your terms. The expectations you set in the minds of consumers will be well aligned with what you can deliver profitably but could drive those that blindly follow your lead into financial ruin.

However, the types of changes represented in this chapter are obviously not simple nor risk free. The complexity of restructuring your business and its offers to create tremendous new value through mobility cannot be underestimated. The impact on processes, systems, organizations, and staffing are significant. You may be well served to get help from those experienced in similar transformations.

Is it worth it?

You have a choice. You can lead and set the rules. Or you can wait for a competitor to lead and define the rules to his benefit and your demise.

 FROM THE REAL WORLD

Making Moby

To best understand how to apply the seven steps, let's consider a hypothetical case study. What if we were a toy company, specializing in stuffed animals, and we wanted to consider "mobilizing" our product. How would we go about it?

Wait a minute! Aren't stuffed animals already mobile? Of course they are. Kids carry their favorite foam-filled friends almost everywhere they go. But, like the camera, which has always been "mobile," stuffed animals could benefit tremendously by becoming even closer to 100% available and by leveraging the power of computing and networking technologies.

For fun, let's consider making our first mobile product a stuffed whale. We'll call him Moby.

Step 1 is to think about digitizing Moby. For a product like a stuffed animal, much of the value comes from the physical reality. Kids

FROM THE REAL WORLD (CONTINUED)

want something cute and cuddly that makes them feel comfortable and safe and helps them fall asleep at night. We can't merely reduce Moby to a bunch of ones and zeros and still be in the stuffed animal business.

But we can look to add digital technology into Moby. Since the PC revolution, many toymakers have added microprocessors into stuffed animals to make them move, talk, sing, and even respond to children in realistic ways. To fully capture the power of mobility in Moby, we should consider how to leverage these technologies.

Step 2 is all about connecting Moby. Since the Internet revolution, a few toymakers have found ways to integrate connectivity into stuffed animals so that the animals interact with information on networked computers. Given our goals for Moby, we should factor these advances into our planning as well.

Step 3 is to evaluate whether we're losing value because we haven't fully mobilized our toys. Do kids take our product every-where they go? Some do, but many don't, or they switch off between different favorites. Would our customers perceive more value if they had our toy with them all the time? From the kids' perspective, maybe not, but let's think about the parents.

Maybe we have an opportunity to focus our marketing on guilty and paranoid parents. We could build on the common concern among today's busy grown-ups that they don't spend enough time with their kids, and their fear that their kids will end up in the wrong place, either accidentally or due to evil intent.

If we could use technology to make our stuffed animal distinctively fun for the kids so they want to take Moby everywhere, then we could use technology to help parents communicate with their kids anytime, anywhere, and make sure they don't stray from safe locations.

Given these goals, let's get specific about the opportunity to digitize and connect Moby:

- Moby could have a limited-capability cell phone built in so that Mommy or Daddy could call their child through this stuffed whale. This would also provide a microphone and speaker for other purposes.
- Moby could have location-sensing capabilities built in (e.g., global positioning system) so he could sense where he is.
- A mobile stuffed animal could have wireless data capabilities built in so he could send and receive data.
- Moby could potentially have a video camera or video screen built in.
- He likely would have some level of computing power and some level of animation robotics.

With this list of capabilities we could design a product offering powerful features for parents:

- The ability (with robust security) to call Moby for an audio or video call from either an Internet-connected computer or a telephone/cell phone.
- Geofencing, so that if Moby travels outside a predefined area, the parent is immediately called and e-mailed, and location tracking is automatically enabled.
- A "nanny camera," enabling the parent (with robust security) to see what is happening through Moby's camera at any time, and even to record pictures or short video clips for future reference.
- Special greetings, which can be recorded by the parent and will randomly play when the child squeezes Moby's tail. The greetings can be recorded with audio and video using the built-in microphone and camera.

For the child, we could offer these fun features:

- Special greetings from Mommy and Daddy.
- Songs and videos that can be played on Moby's speakers and screen. (Mommy or Daddy can purchase additional songs and videos for download to Moby and can remove those that have become too irritating.)
- Warm and friendly gestures, sounds, and messages on the video screen in response to hugs and key phrases.
- Recognition of familiar places based on location data, and Moby expressing excitement about the location (sounds, gestures, and messages like "We're home!" "We're at Grandma's house!" or "We're going to school!" on Moby's screen).

With this combination of features, I believe Moby could be a toy that kids want to take with them everywhere and that their parents will be glad they did!

Step 4 is to limit the product as appropriate for mobility. In general, stuffed animals are relatively limited. We likely will need to make Moby not too small and not too large, but otherwise Moby can probably have just about all the characteristics of your typical stuffed animal.

We've already talked about step 5. We will position Moby to specifically appeal to guilty parents. Given all the technology built in, Moby won't be cheap. We'll need to target Moby to "financially advantaged" guilty parents. Finally, to take full advantage of Moby's abilities, these rich guilty parents will need to be somewhat tech savvy. This positioning will impact our marketing campaigns and the sales channels we use, and perhaps guide us towards some key partnerships to make the product successful.

Step 6 is all about managing the danger of mobility. Moby won't be your typical stuffed animal. He will have power and connectivity needs that are relatively unique. We'll need to ensure that these challenges are easy for our customers to manage.

FROM THE REAL WORLD (CONTINUED)

Speaking of customers, customer support for Moby will go well beyond our existing capabilities. The kinds of complaints customer service is likely to receive from Moby customers will also vary dramatically from those for your typical stuffed whale. Questions about battery life, wireless connectivity, broken components, sea-faring whales (or at least bathtub-faring), Web interfaces, lost passwords, and so on will stump a typical teddy expert.

Most likely, at least at launch, we should consider outsourcing much of the operational challenge to those that are experts in developing Web interfaces, running network businesses, and operating technical support hotlines.

However, the real key to ongoing success with Moby and beyond is step 7: Mobilizing a stuffed animal won't result in just a toy with a camera, screen, global positioning system, and wireless connection built in. Once kids and their parents start playing with Moby, they will uncover for us new value from mobility that we could never predict. They'll find ways to make Moby play fun games we never knew we'd enabled, and they'll ask us to add new features that we never would have imagined.

We will need to be prepared for mobility to completely redefine how kids play with stuffed animals, simply because they are now mobile. And to be prepared to translate those learnings into continued market success!

Notes

1. Sony History www.sony.net/Fun/SH/index.html.
2. "Sony Corporation," *International Directory of Company Histories*, Vol. 40. St. James Press, 2001; www.fundinguniverse.com/company-histories/Sony-Corporation-Company-History1.html.

3. Sony Historical Data, www.sony.net/SonyInfo/IR/library/historical.html.

4. See note 1.

5. Ibid.

6. Ibid.

7. "Sony Targets 6 Million Sales of PSP," www.consolewatcher.com/2005/12/sony-targets-6-million-sales-of-psp/.

8. "The NPD Group Reports Annual 2005 U.S. Video Game Industry Retail Sales," www.npd.com/dynamic/releases/press_060117.html.

9. Apple press release.

10. Pendergast, Sara. 2006. "Pizza." *BookRags*. Retrieved July 15, 2006, from the World Wide Web, www.bookrags.com/history/popculture/pizza-bbbb-03.html.

11. "Domino's Pizza," Wikipedia, http://en.wikipedia.org/wiki/Domino's_Pizza.

12. Domino's Web site, www.dominos.com.

13. www.rateitall.com/t-103-pizza-chains.aspx?age=&zipcode=&gender=&sort=0&pagesize=all.

14. Domino's Investor Presentation, May 2006, from company Web site, www.dominos.com.

15. Ibid.

16. See note 10.

17. www.avis.com/AvisWeb/JSP/global/en/aboutavis/corp_info/historical_chronology.jsp

18. Sprint Web site, www.sprintenterprisemobility.com/mobile_workplace.html.

CHAPTER 6

Digitize

Capture the Power Unleashed by Moore's Law

These days, business runs on bits. It's no longer checks in the mail, but rather electronic transactions. It's no longer cards in a Rolodex, but a customer database. It's no longer numbers in a ledger book, but a financial accounting system.

Whether we're talking about the world's largest corporation or the gas station on the corner, every aspect of business has become digital.

Or has it?

How much information that's critical to the success of your business on a day-to-day or month-to-month basis still exists as ink on paper—or worse, locked up in someone's head? Or on one person's computer that no one else ever sees?

Those islands of information represent business risk and lost opportunity.

Digital data represents tremendous opportunity because it can be relational.

A business card is associated with a person. That person might be an employee of an important customer of yours. That customer has business information, such as the locations you ship products to and how and where they want you to submit invoices so you can get paid. The information on a business card can become digital data that is related to a person, which can be digitally related to his employer, which can be digitally related to locations, which can be digitally related to shipments and invoices. This digital data could be the heart of your revenue stream.

People place orders for companies. Those orders need to be fulfilled, which impacts your inventory. The status of your inventory may impact your production schedule and may cause you to order new supplies. Your production schedule involves your employees. The information on a business card can become digital data that is related to a person, which can be digitally related to her employer, which can be digitally related to orders, which can be digitally related to inventory, which can be digitally related to suppliers and your production schedule and your workers. This digital data could be the heart of your operations.

By interrelating the digital data about your business, you can make better decisions and improve the performance of your business.

Your supplier likes to get paid, but if you're tracking the quality of what he's sending you, and how well he's meeting his commitments, you might want to hold off on paying this supplier until you have a chat.

Your supplier has employees, too. One of them manages your account. You may have his contact information, including his e-mail address, his telephone number, and his cell phone number. You may also have a folder in your e-mail box with all the e-mails he's sent you with wonderful promises. Your electronic calendar may have recorded all the meetings you've had, and it's easy enough to send a meeting request to his calendar for yet another discussion about those wonderful promises.

These little pieces of digital data are powerful because of their relationships—person to employer, to customer, to order, to invoice, to production schedule, to employee schedule, to paycheck, to supplier, to performance metrics, to invoice, to person, to e-mail address, to calendar event, to getting your business operating at it's optimal level.

So any information that is an island rather than being a related piece of data is a lost opportunity for outperforming your competitors. It's like that little rattle that you can't quite clearly hear coming from under the hood that you know is costing a millisecond of hesitation and may even become an expensive failure in the engine of your business.

So, why isn't all the information in your business-related data? Because that's not how we work.

Our salespeople take notes with black ink pens, not laptop keyboards. Our production manager remembers what his vendor promised, but hasn't entered it into any database. We all have yellow sticky pieces of paper with important telephone numbers dangling by one last molecule of adhesive from our computer monitors. And those are the things we've already recognized as information.

What about the data that we hadn't even recognized as such. Where is the best technician for this product—I mean what is his longitude and latitude, the intersection he's driving through right now? What time does UPS expect to deliver that part today? What will the temperature be tomorrow, and how will that impact our scheduled installations? What does Joe like to order at his favorite restaurant, and what's the name of his kid's soccer team?

This is important data! But most companies haven't yet learned how to capture it and use it to beat the competition. Have you?

Thinking clearly and carefully about how your business runs on digital information, bits, data, is the essential first step in capturing the power of mobility. What are the processes that define your business and what data is essential to the success of those processes? What little bits of information are overlooked today, not even captured casually, that if you could factor them into your management of those processes could separate you from the competitive pack?

What's your product? What about it constitutes information that should be managed as data? Is your whole product open to digitization (as happened in the music industry when analog recordings became digital CDs)? What would that take and how are you going to beat your competitors to the punch?

Or are there just seemingly insignificant pieces of information that can be digitized—the owner's manual, the lot number, and serial number? Are there potential outputs from your product that, by digitizing, you could create new value for your customers—maybe information about how your product is used, how often and for what, or how well it's performing its job (validating your customers' investment)? What would it cost to add that in, and how could that translate into value (pricing, loyalty, market share) for your business?

Will digitization create opportunities for you to integrate your product or service with something you've never considered for your business—expanding the market you serve into adjacent spaces? Or are your current partners, suppliers, and customers eyeing your market as a space they can integrate into through digitization?

Capturing all of this information and turning it into relational data is not something that happens overnight at zero cost. Undoubtedly, you'll need to evaluate and prioritize the opportunities. Where are the greatest opportunities to create new value, to stand apart from your competition, and to improve the performance of your business? Where are the greatest threats from important information being lost, or competitors beating you to the punch, or partners stealing your market?

Even once you've prioritized, the business case may be hard to prove. Moore's Law has driven the cost of computing down, but empowering your employees with laptops isn't cheap, and building digital capabilities into your products will increase the unit cost. Can you afford to do it? Can you afford not to?

Once you understand the unavoidable costs, consider the incremental steps you can take to maximize the return on the required investment. If employees have laptops, how can you leverage those capabilities to reduce costs in other areas (office space, filing cabinets, copiers)? How can you drive even greater productivity by equipping each laptop with additional tools (wireless data cards, productivity tools)?

If you've built processing power into your product, can you reduce costs somewhere else by using the compute power to compensate (e.g., automatic recalibration to compensate for a less precise component)? Can you add new features that allow you to charge a premium price?

All of this digitization will also have human costs that should similarly pay rich secondary dividends. Many of us aren't native to this digital age. Expect to invest in training for your employees, either those performing new digitized processes or those assembling new digitized products. But this training will create employees capable of carrying your business forward into the remaining six steps of capturing the power of mobility.

These days, business runs on bits. Does yours?

How to Digitize

Digitizing your business does not involve a magic wand. It requires a step-by-step, need-by-need analysis, implementation plan, and execution. The specific challenges you face will differ from those of your nearest business neighbor, but there are a couple of places you can turn for help.

The first place you might turn is existing literature. Entire books have been written about the opportunities and challenges associated with integrating digital technology into how businesses operate. A few you might consider are *The Social Life of Information* by John Seely Brown and Paul Duguid (Harvard Business School Press, 2002), *Information Literacy and Workplace Performance* by Tom W. Goad (Quorum Books, 2002), *The Virtual Corporation* by William H. Davidow and Michael S. Malone (HarperBusiness, 1992), *The Digital Organization* by James D. Best (John Wiley & Sons, 1997), *The Executive's Guide to Information Technology* by John Baschab and Jon Piot (John Wiley & Sons, 2007), and *Customer Data Integration* by Jill Dyche and Evan Levy (John Wiley & Sons, 2006).

The second place you might turn is to outside help from specialists. Depending on your specific needs, you might turn to a document digitization specialist like Xerox, a consulting firm like Accenture who can help marry processes to technologies, or a mobile specialist like Sprint. Or better yet, start with the specialist firms who are already supporting your business with computer and networking expertise. They likely already understand your business and are already well connected with others in other technology specialist firms.

Digitizing your business is neither painless nor impossible, but it is necessary in today's competitive environment. And it's the critical first step in capturing the power of mobility.

 FROM THE REAL WORLD

Digitizing the Newspaper Business

Pick up a newspaper and your initial reaction is that you're dealing with a relatively low-tech product that hasn't fundamentally changed for centuries.

And in many respects, you'd be absolutely right. The creative process of identifying a newsworthy event, compiling the facts into a meaningful story, and determining the prominence of that story hasn't really changed since Benjamin Franklin's day.

But in so many other ways, the newspaper industry has been transformed time and again by technology advances that both threaten to destroy the industry and create entire new platforms for growth. The most recent series of technology waves transforming the industry started in the 1970s with the introduction of computer front-end systems into the production process. Those arrived as newspapers abandoned lead type for paper or "cold-type" page production, and adopted offset presses—which contributed to innovations in design and increases in color capacity. Desktop publishing on personal computers was introduced in the 1980s. And since the mid-1990s, the basic newspaper business models have been under attack from Internet-based replacements.

Monroe Dodd, an editor for the *Kansas City Star* and editor of *Kansas City: An American Story* (Kansas City Star Books, 1999) remembers "It used to be that a reporter had to carry a lot of dimes for pay phones."

Reporters often had to go to where the news was happening, interview witnesses and experts, dig up any background information they could possibly find, and then call in their notes to the newsroom where rewrite men would compile it all into readable prose.

Monroe notes that today a reporter also can access searchable electronic archives, online databases, and the Internet for background material and can compose and send a completed article from anywhere using his or her laptop and a mobile broadband card.

That electronic copy is then integrated into the computerized pagination system that is used to create on-screen page layout. The system integrates photos and graphics, inserts of advertisements, and then greatly simplifies the process of creating the negative from which the printing plate is created.

As a simple point of comparison, think about photos that appear in the paper. Before desktop publishing, a photo would come out of the darkroom as an 8 × 10 print and would be sent to the engraving department. The engraving department would carve a negative image of the photo into a metal plate that would then be used to print the papers. Today, the digital photo image is integrated into the desktop publishing software, which automatically creates the raster image of the page that becomes the printing plate.

However, even with the dramatic gains in efficiency, the newspaper business is under assault. The Internet threatens every aspect of the industry. Because news can be much more cost-effectively distributed as electronic network bits than as ink on paper, increasing numbers of former newspaper subscribers are turning instead to online news sources. This challenges two of the primary revenue sources for newspapers: subscriptions and advertising revenue. From at least a business model perspective, over the decades, the newspaper has increasingly become a physical container for advertisements that help pay the bills. As readers have left, the value to advertisers has declined, and the resulting revenue hit has been painful.

To add insult to injury, classified ads have more recently come under attack, first in the narrow niche of job placements (from online sites like Monster.com) and now general classified ads from geographically focused consumer ad sites like Craig's List.

Do newspapers have any hope in the face of this technology-driven onslaught?

Monroe notes that "there will always be value in local news gathering. News starts with the news makers, and being there when news happens is part art, part experience, and part relationships. Technology algorithms probably won't ever be able to replace that."

Furthermore, as contextual relevance is integrated into the "newspaper" business, the value of that local perspective will undoubtedly become more prominent. Already newspapers can increase their advertising margins by targeting specific ads to specific parts of town. Locally targeted mobile ads, based on location based technologies, are already starting to appear. Who will first figure out how to leverage contextual relevance to garage sale shoppers, reordering the classified ads based on the shopper's current location?

As has happened so many times over the centuries, technology not only creates challenges, but can also create growth opportunities for those who react well to change.

Case Study

Rand McNally

When I think of going mobile, I most often think of getting in my car and driving somewhere. But heading to a new destination means finding it, which, for centuries has meant breaking out the map. And when I think of maps, I think of Rand McNally.

Rand McNally & Company was founded in 1856. Today, their products are sold in over 60,000 retail outlets and their products are found in 98% of the schools in America, so it's no wonder that their brand is strongly associated with the maps that you and I grew up using to find our way.[1]

But, in today's environment, in addition to using physical, paper-based maps to navigate to new locations, we have more options available. For example, we may use an electronic global positioning system (GPS)-based navigation tool, or turn to an Internet-based mapping tool, or maybe even use a navigation tool on our cell phone.

Is Rand McNally threatened by this shift?

"Absolutely not," says Alan Yefsky, vice president of business strategy and new product development for the company. "We have found that people use different types of mapping tools depending on the situation. Print maps will always be around, and we've used them as a platform to provide continuity and familiarity to consumers as we developed our Internet and mobility based products."[2]

Rand McNally has been a leader through each of the recent technology revolutions. The company's PC-based TripMaker® and StreetFinder® software packages broke new ground, winning awards for the company and establishing market leadership in the new digital personal navigation space. In 1997, the randmcnally .com Web site captured the dynamic power of the Internet, integrating timely road construction and weather updates into the navigation space.

In 2003, Rand McNally introduced Mobile Travel Tools™, providing mapping and navigation tools in a format that could be downloaded to a Java-based mobile phone. The thick-client approach took into account the usability and screen size limitations of a handheld phone, while still providing timely linkage to the content available at randmcnally.com.

Rand McNally has also found ways to leverage the strengths of all of their product lines. StreetFinder® Wireless combines the functional strength of the company's PC-based products with the power of mobility, and also interworks in a unique way with the company's flagship road atlas product.

A traveler may be using the Rand McNally Road Atlas during a long distance trip, but may reach a midpoint in his destination where he wants to find a restaurant or hotel. By entering an express access code from the paper atlas into StreetFinder Wireless, the traveler is immediately zoomed in to the local street maps and can dynamically search for the destination.

"Since we operate across technology platforms, we've paid close attention to the strengths and challenges of each platform and how that translates into how people actually use different types of navigation products," notes Gary Lancina, Rand McNally's vice president of marketing. "For example, randmcnally.com is a great tool for planning a trip, but people are most comfortable using our print products while en route. Our Road Atlas is great for getting from city to city and our Street Guides are great for finding your way around your hometown, but when you arrive in a new city, our GPS-based products allow you to act like a local anywhere in America.''

To build on the company's strong presence in the traditional paper-based navigation space, Rand McNally has extended its grid system across all of its products, paper and electronic. This commonality enables easy transitions from Internet to paper to mobile, as Gary described above, but also provides a sense of continuity and comfort as customers adopt new technologies.

The company has also learned a lot about how different types of people use the same products differently. For example, the average consumer probably drives the same route in the same parts of town day after day, week after week, but occasionally will venture out to a new part of town for a kids' soccer tournament or cultural event. This customer will rely on Rand McNally's street-level guides to figure out which highways to take, which side of the road to exit, down to the last turn into the sports park. A local delivery driver, however, is an expert at getting from any part of town to any other, but will turn to the street guide for the last quarter mile to his destination.

This long-standing understanding of how customers rely on naviga-tion tools has translated into Rand McNally's mobile tools—from how they are designed for different users to how they are marketed, and finally to how they are integrated with the company's core products.

One of the challenges any company will face that is moving from traditional physical products to new technology products is prepar-ing for new customer service needs.

Rand McNally's interactions with customers have evolved from getting letters in the mail from people wondering why their 20-year-old road atlas isn't current any more to now getting live phone calls from customers trying to navigate a new city. Some customers even expected to be able to call the toll-free number on their road atlas to get free live directions to their destination. Alan notes that "as in any business, consumer expectations are very high. We needed to adapt the strategies we had developed for addressing consumer concerns with traditional 'analog' products to address new kinds of issues specific to the digital and mobile environment."

Alan also explains that Rand McNally never underestimates the customer—they are the ones who really understand what is needed. They can provide rich feedback that translates into new opportunities for differentiation and value creation.

He cites the example of local delivery dispatchers who were regularly using randmcnally.com to figure out the best route, then copying the directions into a text message to the drivers' phones. By learning from the customer, Rand McNally was able to develop and introduce a new text-to-phone feature for their Web-based service.

Bottom line: Rand McNally has clearly executed on the seven steps described in this book. They are capturing the power of mobility while building on the strong foundation of a powerful legacy halfway through its second century. This company doesn't see it as choosing between technologies, but rather as finding the best way to help people do things they couldn't do before.

"In our business, it's clear that human behavior is messy," Alan observes. "As technology evolves, winners figure out how to use the right technology to make life a little bit less messy."

RAND MCNALLY'S MOBILIZED PRODUCTS[3]

So far, Rand McNally has built mobility into three product lines: Rand McNally Mobile Navigator (MONA), StreetFinder® Wireless, and Rand McNally Traffic. The product desriptions that follow are provided by Rand McNally.

Rand McNally Mobile Navigator (MONA)

Rand McNally MONA gives you instant, audible, accurate turn-by-turn voice directions on your GPS-enabled mobile phone.

- Avoid the cost of getting lost with voice-prompted, turn-by-turn navigation and automatic rerouting for missed turns.

- Easily and efficiently enter addresses online or on the phone.

- Locate and route to the nearest gas station, ATM, restaurant, and other points of interest.

- Save money—Rand McNally MONA works on your existing mobile phone equipment.

Rand McNally StreetFinder ® Wireless

Easy to use, impossible to live without, StreetFinder® Wireless gives you access to maps, directions, and a directory of points of interest, wherever you are, all on the convenience of your mobile phone. Ideal for getting around town, perfect for travel.

With StreetFinder® Wireless on your phone you can:

- Save time. Quickly and easily locate addresses and points of interest in your area, and get maps, directions, and location information to help you get there.

- Be flexible—plans change, don't be caught without alternatives. StreetFinder® Wireless is always as close as your mobile phone.

- Act like a local—even when traveling! Want to find the nearest ATM, bank, or restaurant to your hotel? Need a reservation? Get it done yourself.

- Pinpoint your location. If your phone has GPS capabilities, StreetFinder® Wireless automatically maps your location, and can provide you with a listing of local restaurants, hotels, coffee shops, gas stations, and the like. Makes getting directions easy!

- Get more from your printed maps. By using Express Access Codes built into the Rand McNally Road Atlas, you can quickly and easily use StreetFinder Wireless to get local street detail and points of interest for any area in the country.

Rand McNally Traffic

Rand McNally Traffic puts you in control. It helps you plan, anticipate, and arrive worry free. Get real-time traffic updates on your mobile phone. Know about traffic on your specific route … before it's too late.

Available every day, all day, accurate up-to-the-minute information with traffic maps by region, city, road, or neighborhood showing:

- Accidents
- Traffic congestion
- Average road speeds (in select cities)
- Toll backups
- Road or lane closures
- Public transit delays

The handy Commute Wizard function lets you save a start and end point for fast and easy access anywhere, anytime.

Notes

1. www.randmcnally.com/rmc/company/cmpProfile.jsp.
2. www.randmcnally.com/rmc/company/cmpTimeLine.jsp.
3. *Source:* Rand McNally & Company.

CHAPTER 7

Connect

Capture the Power Unleashed by Metcalfe's Law

The Internet revolutionized how business gets done, not just because it extended the value of digitization onto data networks, but because of the reach of connectivity that was involved. Unlike previous data networks, the Internet was not limited to one location, or one company, or a limited group of collaborators, but rather it was a network for the world.

Because the Internet was everyone's network and cut across traditional boundaries, the digital value that had been captured within companies could now be amplified by extending it beyond those companies. This translated into three dominant business models from the mid-1990s to today.

The first successful business model is represented by Amazon.com. In 1995, Jeff Bezos launched "the world's largest bookstore." In reality, there was virtually nothing real about Amazon's bookstore—it was almost all digitized virtual reality. Bezos combined digital data about the books that were available from publishers with an attractive digital online storefront and the capability to accept digital payments using credit cards and Amazon.com was up and running. As of the third quarter of 2006, Amazon was reporting more than $2 billion a quarter in sales. I'd say it worked.

What Amazon.com did was not radical by today's standards, but it could be done only because the piece parts had been digitized (information about books, pictures of book covers, and credit card transactions), and Amazon.com could further use digital technology to efficiently fulfill the logistics of a customer's order (feeding orders to the warehouse for picking and packing, coordinating with FedEx for shipping and tracking).

Obviously, many others have followed in Amazon's footsteps, creating successful Internet e-commerce businesses. For example, Barnes & Noble Booksellers, an obvious target of Amazon's success, has been very aggressive with eCommerce. In the third quarter of 2006, nearly 10% of Barnes & Noble's $1.1 billion in revenue came through barnesandnoble.com.

The second successful business model is represented by Yahoo .com. Yahoo created a "portal" business that helped connect people to digital content. Much of that content is from traditional sources, such as news bureaus and traditional media companies. Yahoo leverages the digitization of this content to present customers with content they're comfortable with in a more dynamic (up to the instant) and interactive (customers have more control over what they receive and how and when) fashion that makes the original product even more valuable to the customer. Yahoo's primary revenue stream, as has been true with traditional media, is advertising. However, the digital and networked nature of Internet ads provides the advertiser with a much higher confidence that the right consumers are seeing the ads and better feedback that the ads are translating into consumer action. This makes Internet ads more valuable to advertisers. Yahoo reported $1.6 billion in revenues in the third quarter of 2006.

Yahoo's success demonstrates the opportunity to take a traditional product and, by digitizing it and extending it to customers across a network, magnify the product's value.

Many have followed in Yahoo's footsteps, with Apple Computer being a high-profile example. Apple reported $485 million in sales of "other music products" in the second quarter of 2006. This primarily consists of music and video sales through the iTunes music store.

Amazon, Yahoo, and Apple have each disrupted existing industries (book retailing, publishing, and music respectively) by taking digitized product information or the products themselves and using that digitization and networking to improve the customers' experience.

The third successful business model is represented by eBay. eBay connects people in new ways across networks. Specifically, eBay primarily connects buyers and sellers to perform their transactions in new and more efficient ways. eBay makes it easy for the members of its community to digitize all aspects of their interactions, from presenting product information and pictures to talking real time about the product (using eBay's Skype technology) to processing a digital payment (using eBay's PayPal transaction processing services). For the third quarter of 2006, eBay reported $1.4 billion in revenue.

Many others have followed in eBay's footsteps, making it easier for people to connect in new and exciting ways by simplifying the uploading and sharing of digital content and finding others with similar interests. Two currently prominent examples are MySpace (acquired by News Corporation for $580 million in 2005) and YouTube (acquired by Google for $1.6 billion in 2006).

eBay, MySpace, and YouTube have no value without the participants in their communities and yet they have created tremendous value by leveraging networking and making it easy for participants to digitize and share their own products.

Now, in 2007, most of the Internet buzz is about something people reference as Web 2.0. There are many definitions of what this means, but I would call out one particular new characteristic that has set these new Internet participants apart—the ability to integrate pieces of different services together into something new. The common phrase for this is "mashups," and these services often use new technology called Web Services and protocols such as XML (extensible markup language), SOAP (simple object access protocol), and REST (representational state transfer).

What does all this mean? It means that someone can take a data feed across the network from one source with, for example, real estate listings, and data feed from another source with housing market pricing data, geocoding data from another source to translate everything into longitude and latitude coordinates, and then present it on a map using Google's mapping service. I can do this as a tool just for myself or my employees, or I can open it up as a service for the whole world to use.

So, now that you've digitized your business, how will open networks amplify the value of your digitized data?

Is your product now a virtual digital product that can be sold and delivered across the network at nearly zero production cost? Is information about your product now digitized in a way that can be delivered across the network to customers or partners to increase sales or improve customer service and loyalty? Can you leverage networks to facilitate connecting with key communities (employees, channel partners, suppliers, customers) in ways that create value for them and for you?

What information are you willing to let across the network? What will you allow employees to access? What will you allow partners to access? What will you allow authenticated customers to access? What will you allow the whole world to access?

In what ways do you want each group to be able to access that data? Something they can "see but not touch" (e.g., as an image file)? Data they can download but not manipulate (e.g., as an uneditable portable document format [PDF] file)? Data they can download and work with (e.g., as a spreadsheet file)? A data stream they can "mash up" into a Web 2.0 application?

How will you enforce the policies we just discussed? How will you secure sensitive data? How will you authenticate authorized users? How will you protect your intellectual property rights?

These are not simple questions, and the implementation of the answers is well beyond the scope of this book. But they are critical questions to answer and successfully implement.

Choosing to share too little will likely open the door for your competitors to gain an advantaged position in the marketplace. Choosing to share too much can destroy the value of your product and intellectual property. Failing to securely implement what you decide will result in failing to gain a favored position and also destroying corporate value.

How do you decide what to share, with whom, and in what fashion?

Start with the imperatives. Have your competitors taken steps that you must match to maintain parity in the marketplace? Do you have an opportunity to take their actions one step further to gain advantage without destroying value?

Next, look for opportunities to improve your business performance. Are their networked information solutions to statements from your sales channels ("I could sell more if . . ."), your customers ("I would buy more if . . ."), your production group ("We could create a higher value product at a lower cost if . . ."), or your support organization ("We would get fewer customer problem calls if . . .")? The benefits claimed may not always be enough to justify the investment, but it is critical to listen for these opportunities.

Once you understand the opportunities and requirements, you can move toward implementation. Given the complexity of successfully and securely implementing networked computing initiatives, if you do not already have experienced staff on board, this would be a great time to engage outside help. As always, a great place to start is with the partners who already support your technology needs, who understand your business and are probably well connected with other experts. Global information technology (IT) leaders such as IBM, EDS, and Hewlett Packard are well versed in all of the applications and technologies involved in networking your business. Application specialists, such as EMC, Verisign, and Entrust may also be worth considering, depending on your opportunities and needs.

And it never hurts to read up on the opportunities and challenges in connecting your business with the world. You may consider titles such as *Digital Capital* by Don Tapscott, David Ticoll, and Alex Lowy (Harvard Business School Press, 2000), *Service Orient or Be Doomed!* by Jason Bloomberg and Ronald Schmelzer (John Wiley & Sons, 2006), *Out of the Box* by John Hagel III (Harvard Business School Press, 2002), *Information Rules* by Carl Shapiro and Hal R. Varian (Harvard Business School Press, 1998), and *Unleashing the Killer App* by Larry Downes and Chunka Mui (Harvard Business School Press, 1998).

Successfully implementing networking initiatives will enable you to maximize the value of your digitized data and will prepare you for the next step in capturing the power of mobility.

FROM THE REAL WORLD

Digitizing and Connecting Magazines

At the beginning of 1995, when my partners and I founded Digital Frontiers, a Web consulting firm, one of the first companies we called on was PennWell Publishing. PennWell was, and is, publisher of a diverse portfolio of magazines. However, the company is best known as the publisher of the *Oil and Gas Journal*, a 105-year-old weekly publication that keeps the entire oil and gas industry in the know.

Obviously, PennWell had seen plenty of change in the publishing industry in their time, but that didn't mean they were quick to abandon their highly successful existing business models. Over time, we were able to convince them to begin to experiment, and before long they'd jumped in with both feet. We partnered to launch OGJOnline, a new Web-based online service specifically designed to appeal to the conservative nature of the oil and gas industry. As part of this launch, we converted ten years' worth of the weekly publication's back issues to online digital format to provide the kind of archival searching that had previously been virtually impossible for PennWell's subscribers.

To address the conservatism of the *Oil and Gas Journal*'s subscribers, we developed a custom solution with a locked-down Web browser and dial-up software to ensure that oil company employees weren't "exposed" to the "dangers" of the Internet. Response was very positive. The initial business model mirrored the subscription model of the print magazine. Over time, advertising revenues became increasingly prominent in PennWell's online activities. Today, PennWell operates over 60 Web sites[1] supporting their 45+ publications. PennWell has also launched PennEnergy, a Web-based market for surplus equipment for the energy industry.

Obviously, PennWell's early adoption of digital and Web technology has positioned them well to grow their business and capture emerging opportunities.

But, the fascinating aspect of PennWell's journey has been the transformation that has occurred in their business. Online publishing radically changed PennWell's editorial perspectives. For the Web, the weekly publishing timeline could be thrown out the window. When content was ready, it could run online. Online content was no longer constrained by column lengths and traditional structures, and online-only features became possible and appealing.

The experience for readers also changed. At the time, most companies had libraries that kept back issues of all important publications for easy reference by employees. As publications like the *Oil and Gas Journal* moved online, these periodical libraries became much less critical. Many readers began looking for the online version of the publication to arrive, often days before it would show

FROM THE REAL WORLD (CONTINUED)

up in physical form. And as OGJOnline grew in popularity, what had started as a one-way publication became a vibrant industry online community.

The change wasn't without risks and challenges.

Especially in the early days, it was hard to deliver an aesthetically pleasing and usable online publication that came close to matching the quality product that PennWell was accustomed to delivering. There also were real concerns about the value of the content, copyright protections, and later, as the community became more active, editorial control over everything appearing on OGJOnline.

However, I'm sure that PennWell is thankful for their early initiative in taking their publications online and creating one of the first industry portals in the world.

Case Study

MapQuest

In 1994, printing giant R. R. Donnelly & Sons formed an entrepreneurial start-up called GeoSystems Global Corporation, which in 1996 launched the MapQuest.com Web service. The rest, as they say, is history. MapQuest became the go-to source for maps and directions for the growing online population. In 1999, AOL acquired MapQuest for more than $1 billion, but that didn't stop the innovation at the company, which continued to operate as a separate division.[2] As MapQuest's online audience has gone mobile, the company has seen the opportunity to invest in building mobility into their product so that the company remains accessible, relevant, and usable wherever MapQuest's users go.

"We actually saw both offensive and defensive reasons to extend our mapping leadership into mobility," reports Alan Beiagi, the director and general manager of MapQuest Wireless. "We recognize that the user profile of mobile users is slightly different from our traditional MapQuest base, meaning that mobility provides a way to extend our reach into this market. We also recognize that if we don't take the mapping experience mobile, others will, and our brand and leadership position will be damaged, so mobilizing became a competitive imperative."

Mapping and navigation, of course are a very natural choice for mobility. Taking MapQuest's capabilities mobile has created immediate value for the company's customers. But a critical issue for MapQuest is how to translate that customer value into shareholder value.

As a traditional Internet company, MapQuest's primary revenue stream has been online advertising. The PC Web browser screen provides plenty of real estate to wrap beautiful, enticing ads around the content MapQuest's customers are seeking. However, when that experience moves to a small mobile device, screen real estate becomes scarce and users become intolerant of anything inhibiting finding their way.

In entering the space, MapQuest has initially adopted the mobile applications industry model of charging users a monthly subscription fee to use MapQuest's solutions. This approach has been fine for an initial foray, but the company recognizes that monthly fees create a barrier to the kind of broad adoption that the company has enjoyed with the free MapQuest.com service. A different approach is required long term.

Alan notes that "it's critical to understand your customer. Why are they using your product? How are they using your product? How does that create value and for whom? When you deeply understand these factors, you can tailor your product and your business model to capture the most value.''

MapQuest is developing a contextually relevant business model. Why do people use a mobile navigation tool? Because they need to find their way. And often they need to find the place where they want to go. Using MapQuest's mobile products, a user can search for a hotel for the night or a restaurant for dinner or the nearest electronics store. Knowing that the hotel/restaurant/store exists is good, finding it is better, but often we want to call ahead to make reservations or check to see if what we want is in stock. Clicking through to call translates into an immediate highly qualified lead that's valuable to the business, translating into a revenue opportunity for MapQuest.

This points to the continuing evolution of advertising. First, we had broadcast and print advertising, where value was measured simply by exposure and the most the advertiser could hope for was awareness. Next came Internet advertising where value was measured by click-throughs, where advertisers hope customers will be interested in learning more and maybe even buying. Now, with contextually relevant mobile advertising, value is measured by capturing customers when they are in the very process of the decision, delivering to advertisers highly qualified customers wanting to make a purchase.

For MapQuest, revenue opportunities are not limited to the mobile space. A guiding factor in the company's pursuit of mobile opportunities has been seamless integration between the desktop and mobile experiences. With 54 million users of MapQuest.com, the company has a great start to building a base of mobile customers. The company has worked hard to optimize each platform for its strengths. Customers can start by using MapQuest at their desktop to research and plan a trip, and then transfer the fruits of those efforts into MapQuest's mobile products for easy access to relevant information on the go.

CASE STUDY (CONTINUED)

Just as importantly, the company has looked for ways to leverage the strengths of the mobile platform to bring customers back to the MapQuest Web-based service. A great example is MapQuest Navigator, which uses the global positioning system (GPS) capabilities built into Sprint Nextel phones to provide users with turn-by-turn, voice-guided driving directions.

The fact that MapQuest Navigator is currently available only to Sprint Nextel customers points to one of the biggest challenges MapQuest has faced in building mobility into their products. Within the mobile market, there seem to be an infinite number of combinations of network capabilities, handset capabilities, and operating system capabilities. MapQuest has broken the market down into four tiers by technology capability. Almost all cell phones can send and receive text messages. About half have some form of Web browsing capability. About a third can download an application, and less than one tenth currently have GPS capabilities.

On one hand, these differences create an opportunity to segment the market and develop specific products for the different types of users who naturally gravitate toward the devices with specific capabilities. But on the other hand, this diversity creates development costs and challenges that were beyond what MapQuest expected when they headed down the mobility path.

To help manage these complexities, MapQuest turned to two companies much more experienced in working with the countless varieties of technology combinations. MapQuest turned to Zingy to launch the MapQuest Mobile downloadable application, and turned to Telmap for help building the MapQuest Navigator GPS-based, voice-guided navigation application.

Alan acknowledges that having partners that understood the varied environments has been critical to MapQuest's success. "It's critical that we focus on our strengths and on seamless integration with our desktop products. Zingy and Telmap helped us maintain that focus.''

Sometimes even a navigation leader needs help finding its way through a new neighborhood!

MapQuest's Mobilized Products

The following product descriptions are provided by MapQuest, Inc.

MapQuest offers three products that capture the power of mobility: MapQuest Navigator, MapQuest Mobile, and the company's free WAP service for Web-enabled phones.

MapQuest Navigator represents leading edge technology in mobile navigation and gives you a powerful new level of convenience that is available when you need it most.

Enjoy in-car navigation in the palm of your hand!

MapQuest Navigator turns your phone into a full GPS Navigation system.

- Hear voice-guided, turn-by-turn directions right on your phone.
- Superior navigation display with full moving maps that automatically zoom in and out at the right time.
- Use full pedestrian navigation that ignores vehicle turning and one-way driving.
- Receive guidance and automatic rerouting even when you are out of network range.
- Find over 15 million of points of interest including restaurants, hotels, and theaters from the MapQuest.com database.
- Locate addresses, intersections, or zip codes with ease.
- Customize routes by finding the fastest or shortest route, or avoid toll roads and highways.

- Easy-to-read dynamic color maps that move as you follow the turn-by-turn directions.
- Zoom in or out, and pan and point on a map.
- Save frequently visited destinations in "My Places" menu.
- Receive phone calls without interrupting navigation.
- Make phones calls while navigating on select handsets.
- Direct dial to any of MapQuest's 15 million points of interest.

MapQuest Mobile offers U.S. and Canadian coverage from the world's leading online map provider. Instantly find your way with interactive color maps, step-by-step instructions, reverse directions, and recall of recent addresses.

The newest enhancements to MapQuest Mobile include:

- MapQuest's points of interest: Find over 15 million points of interest including restaurants, hotels, and theaters from the MapQuest.com database.
- Multipoint routing: Select multipoints along your route and receive step-by-step directions.
- Find places, get maps and step-by-step directions for Canada!
- Click to call a business directly from MapQuest Mobile (availability limited to certain carriers).
- Access recent locations and multiroutes: Access your most recent places and multiroutes.
- Save locations and multiroutes to favorites: Save your places and multiroutes to your favorites folder.
- Pedestrian navigation: Get directions for walking routes.
- Choose advanced routing options: Optimize your route by choosing the shortest time or distance and/or avoid tolls.

Next time you look up MapQuest directions, don't print them. Click on the "Send to Cell" link at the top of the page.

Case Study (continued)

MapQuest Mobile was created in partnership with Zingy, one of the best-known publishers of consumer applications for mobile phones.

MapQuest® Navigator turns your phone into a full in-car navigation system. It helps you find places, get maps, and receive voice-guided, turn-by-turn directions using the latest GPS technology on your mobile phone.

Decide where you want to go and MapQuest Navigator will guide you there—quickly, easily, anywhere, anytime!

MapQuest free WAP service enables users with Web-enabled mobile phone or PDAs to access a "right-sized" version of Map-Quest optimized for their phones. Users simply visit wap.map-quest.com using their mobile browser to find any destination, get detailed maps, and get turn-by-turn directions. In addition, with MapQuest's "Send to Cell" service, users can search for places and create maps and directions on their home or office desktop, and send that information to their cell phones by clicking on the "Send to Cell" link conveniently found through the MapQuest.com site. Then, while on the road, they can quickly access the information on their mobile device via a simple text link, and be directed to their turn-by-turn directions and detailed maps, all "right-sized" for their cell phone's Web browser.

Notes

1. www.pennwellpetroleumgroup.com/sites/index.cfm.
2. http://company.mapquest.com/corporate/2.html.

CHAPTER 8

Evaluate
How Is the Value of Your Product or Service Limited?

obility creates value above and beyond digitization and networking in three forms:

1. By increasing the availability of a product or service.

2. By using the immediate context of the product or service use to improve the relevance of the product or service to the customer.

3. By reducing the cost of a product or service.

Now that you have digitized and connected to create value for your business, you must evaluate ways in which you can increase that value through the increased availability, contextual relevance, or reduced cost promised by mobility.

Increasing Availability

What percentage of the time is your product or service fully available to your customers?

For a product, availability usually means how often your product is within their reach with its full capabilities. Do they take it with them everywhere they go? Does your product work anywhere, or are there special requirements, such as needing to be plugged in, needing to be connected to a certain kind of network, or only able to be used under certain conditions?

For a service, availability usually means when and where your customers can use your service. Do they need to go to a certain location? Are there only certain times and days that the service is available? Do your customers need something (e.g., a computer or telephone) to access your service?

What could you do to increase the availability of your product or service?

What could you do so that your customers would take your product everywhere they go? What could you do to reduce or eliminate the current requirements or conditions for your product's use?

If you have fully digitized your product, would it be possible to converge your product into a mobile phone so that your customers literally will take it with them everywhere they go? If not, but your product requires networked information, is it possible to build mobile wireless networking into your product so that it's fully available all the time?

What could you do so that your customers can use your service everywhere they go? Have you digitized your service and networked it so that your customers can access it over the Internet? If so, could you optimize that Internet access to work well with the small screen and limited keyboard of a mobile phone so that they can access it anywhere, anytime they have their phone?

If your service involves direct interaction between your employees and your customers, what can you do to make your employees available no matter where or when your customers need them? Is it possible for your service to be delivered over the telephone or the Internet? If not, can your employees become mobile to go to where your customers are? Can wireless technologies enable you to establish very short term (for a few hours, a day, a weekend, a week) service locations for special events to be where you know your customers are going to be, providing them with highly valued convenience?

Evaluating any of these options requires a deep understanding of your customers' desires and frustrations. How and when and where do they really want to use your product or service? How well does your current offer match those desires? How well could adding mobility to your product or service better align with your customers' needs?

What about your product or service currently frustrates your customers? How much of that frustration is associated with availability—where, when, and under what conditions they can use your product or service? Could these limitations be overcome by adding mobility into your product or service?

How could you translate better alignment with your customers' desires or elimination of their frustrations into value for your company? Will you be able to increase the price? Will you sell more? Will your customers be more loyal? Will you be able to reduce customer care costs or reduce billing disputes and unpaid customer invoices? Can you put a dollar figure on this value creation to help justify any necessary investment?

Contextual Relevance

Is there an opportunity to improve your customer's perception and value of your product or service by making it more relevant to the context in which they are using it?

Could your product create value by performing differently based on where your customer is using it, whom they are with, what is on their calendar, what the weather is, or what time it is? Could you make your product easier to use if it automatically adapted to the situation rather than having to be either reconfigured by your customer or tolerated in a suboptimal state? Could your product perform better, providing better results if it knew the current context and performed appropriately?

Could your service create value by taking into account where your customer is, what time it is where they are, whom they are with, what the weather is or forecast to be, or when their next appointment is (and where)? Could you save your customer some trouble or some time by automatically collecting this information instead of requiring them to tell you or type it in? Could your service perform better, providing better results if your company automatically knew the current context and performed appropriately?

Can you build into your product or service technologies to provide context, such as the current location or the current time? Can you tap into existing network-based sources to determine the weather or the traffic or the status of your customer's flight? Can you integrate with other products that your customer is using to know (with your customers' permission) what their calendar looks like or with whom they have just met or are about to meet? Can you correlate information across your customers to create value by knowing that two customers are or will be together and making your product or service work better for them together?

These questions are at the heart of evaluating the opportunity to increase the value of your product or service through contextual relevance enabled by mobility.

How will your business benefit from this increased relevance? Will you be able to increase the price? Will you sell more? Will your customers be more loyal? Will you be able to reduce customer care costs or reduce billing disputes and unpaid customer invoices? Can you put a dollar figure on this value creation to help justify any necessary investment?

Reduced Costs

Is there an opportunity to increase your customers' appreciation for the value of your product or service by reducing its price?

If you can converge your product into a cell phone, does that translate into dramatic reductions in manufacturing and repair costs? If you can deliver your product as bits, can you similarly dramatically reduce all costs associated with the physical components of your product? If your product will have network connectivity built in, can you replace more expensive components with less expensive components and compensate by receiving updated accurate information over the network?

Will mobilizing your service make your employees more efficient? Will it accelerate information flow, resulting in fewer costly mistakes? Will it eliminate expensive paper processes and duplication of effort?

Will mobilization reduce data entry requirements and associated human errors?

How much of these cost reductions do you need to apply to paying for your mobility investment? How much are you willing to pass on to customers as price reductions?

What Does It Take?

There are a number of levels of complexity possible in building mobility into your product or service.

The simplest level is to provide your service employees with effective tools for taking your service mobile and turning them loose to serve your customers. You'll likely need to invest in mobile phones, laptops, wireless data cards, and the appropriate voice and data plan to keep your employees connected and productive wherever they go. Wireless carriers can help you select the best tools and plan for what your business needs.

The next level is to enable your now mobile workers with solutions to be more effective when they're in the field. Sprint is the leading provider of mobile business solutions and offers dozens of applications ranging from simple navigation and messaging to resource tracking to credit card processing to work order and dispatch management, to vertical solutions unique to your industry, but other carriers are also developing portfolios of business solutions.

The next level of complexity is to ensure that your Web-enabled capabilities will work well for your employees and customers when they are using their mobile devices. The official standards group for the World Wide Web provides a profile for designing Web sites to work well with mobile devices. This profile is available at www.w3

.org/TR/css-mobile/. Another excellent resource is the Global Authoring Practices for the Mobile Web, available at www.passani .it/gap. Finally, a collection of large wireless industry players have created a company called dotmobi to make the mobile device as useful as a PC for browsing and data applications. They offer a collection of "Switch On!" guides for developing for the mobile Web. These are available at http://pc.mtld.mobi/mobilenet/dotmobi_guides.html.

You may decide to develop applications specifically to run on mobile devices rather than simply using a Web interface. This provides a higher level of control over security and performance and may enable your product to work well even when the network isn't. Most carriers have developers' programs to support folks developing for the devices on their network. A number of valuable resources are typically available through these programs to create, test, and deploy applications for devices on the carriers' networks.

If your product is a physical product that cannot be easily converged into a mobile phone, but that you want to consider building mobility in, then you may want to pursue a variety of options.

One is to embed mobile network connectivity into your product. You'll likely want to align with one carrier per global region to simplify your development, certification testing, and support. You'll want to work closely with the business development group at each carrier.

Another, complementary approach is to build mobility-enabling technology into your product. This could include alternative sources of power, such as solar panels and fuel cells, memory for storing data being transmitted and received, global positioning system (GPS) location tracking sensors, or any of a variety of other sensors that could provide important contextual information to increase the value of your product through increased relevance. Tremendous strides are being made in making these components cost effective, energy efficient, small, and robust for embedding into products. For example, Epson recently introduced an ultrasensitive GPS module that is only 6 mm by 7 mm by 1.3 mm in size, Yamaha recently introduced a 2 mm by 2 mm three-axis geomagnetic sensor for determining directional movement in mobile devices, and Hewlett Packard has developed memory the size of a grain of rice that can store up to 4 megabytes of data and requiring no external power.

Understanding the value that can be created by mobilizing your product will help you evaluate the different options you have for doing so. As we'll see in the next step in capturing the power of mobility, often it's deciding what *not* to do that will be critical in delivering real value to your customers and creating value for your shareholders.

FROM THE REAL WORLD

The Mobility Declaration of Independence

As a creative illustration of the revolutionary power of mobility and of the forces against which mobility is in revolt, in July 2006, I introduced a Mobility Declaration of Independence on the Law-of-Mobility.com blog. I modeled this new declaration after the American Declaration of Independence of 1776. Historically, the Americans were revolting against a ruler they considered a tyrant, so it was also necessary for me to introduce the tyrant of the Big Bell Dogma against which mobility is rebelling.

FROM THE REAL WORLD (CONTINUED)

BIG BELL DOGMA

Clearly, mobility provides freedom from "fixedness." As we develop our list of charges against our oppressor, they will largely or entirely be the injustice of being tied to a specific location.

But what is forcing us into this fixed state?

As much as anything, I think what we're struggling against is a mind-set that is firmly embedded in how products and processes are designed and in how businesses operate.

For fun, I'd like to call this oppressing force "Big Bell Dogma."

According to Wikipedia, "dogma" is belief or doctrine held by a religion, ideology, or any kind of organization to be authoritative and not to be disputed or doubted.

I think this well captures the mindset against which we fight. It is the belief held by product development groups and by those that define processes that "of course it can't move, it never has."

"Big Bell" is a reference to the way AT&T built the telephone network over the past century or so. As mentioned, not all oppression against mobility is related to telephony, but I think the mind-set of that old company well reflects the mind-set we're fighting against.

In *Nerds 2.0.1*, this mind-set is well reflected by this quote from Len Kleinrock, one of the key players in the establishment of the ARPAnet, which would become the Internet: "I would say, 'Please give us good data communications,' and they would reply, 'The United States is a copper mine—we have phone lines everywhere so use the telephone network.' I would counter, 'But you don't understand, it takes 25 seconds to set up a call, you charge me for a minimum three minutes, and all I want is to send a millisecond of data.' Their reply was, 'Go away, children, the revenue stream from data transmission is dwarfed by that of our voice traffic.' So the children went away and created the Internet!"

Back in 1995 when I cofounded an Internet start-up, I encountered this same mentality within the businesses that we were selling to— a sense that communications would never change. Even though the original AT&T had been broken up 11 years earlier, when I asked one of our customers who his local telephone company was, his retort was "AT&T, of course!"

These examples are specific to the Internet, but I believe this "dogma" extends to a bias against mobility as well. The copper and fiber networks that have been built by the telecom industry represent truly "buried" costs that have historically translated into tremendous wealth creation. Obviously, these assets are well suited to continue to serve a purpose in the information economy, but newer technologies provide tremendous advantages for many applications that have traditionally been served by these fixed facilities.

Although there is still a company called AT&T, I think you recognize that the "new AT&T" is not really the "bad guy" I'm referencing here.

The original AT&T was first dismantled in 1984 as the result of a Justice Department antitrust action. The company that retained the AT&T name continued to self-destruct, first splitting out its innovation arm as Lucent and its computing arm as NCR and later spinning off AT&T Wireless.

The company formerly known as Southwestern Bell was one of the "Baby Bells" created in 1984 out of AT&T and has been working hard to recreate much of what the original Ma Bell had been, most dramatically acquiring the remains of AT&T and taking on that moniker in the past few years.

From the Real World (continued)

However, this new AT&T is a very different company that has benefited as much from the fall of the old Ma Bell as anyone has. I'm not saying that the new AT&T is immune to the defensiveness described above as "Big Bell Dogma" (are any of us?), but I ask that no one equate the two.

What we fight against is the mind-set represented by those who defend the tethering of products and processes to specific places. This mind-set is fueled by the investments that have been made that establish power in the companies, departments, and individuals that stand in the way of mobilizing our lives and our businesses. These investments are not always in hard assets, but often are investments of time and experience to establish intellectual and relational assets.

We should expect our assault on these "fixed" ways to be defended to the death.

So, at least personally for me, this "Big Bell Dogma" is a fair representation of the oppressor that is holding back the independence promised by Mobility.

The Declaration

When in the course of human events it becomes necessary for people to dissolve the technological bonds which have connected them with a specific place for a specific task and to assume among the powers of the earth, the free and mobile status to which the Laws of Nature and of Nature's God entitle them, a decent respect to the opinions of mankind requires that they should declare the causes which impel them to the separation.

We hold these truths to be self-evident:

- That all men are created equal.
- That they are endowed by their Creator with certain unalienable Rights.

- That among these are Life, Liberty, and the pursuit of Happiness.

- That to secure these rights, Technologies are implemented among Men, deriving their just powers from the consent of the enabled.

- That whenever any Form of Technology becomes destructive of these ends, it is the Right of the People to alter or to replace it, and to implement new Technology, laying its foundation on such principles and organizing its powers in such form, as to them shall seem most likely to effect their Safety and Happiness.

Prudence, indeed, will dictate that Technologies long established should not be changed for light and transient causes; and accordingly all experience hath shown that mankind are more disposed to suffer, while evils are sufferable than to right themselves by abolishing the tools to which they are accustomed. But when a long train of abuses and usurpations, pursuing invariably the same Object evinces a design to reduce them under absolute Despotism, it is their right, it is their duty, to throw off such Technology, and to provide new Enablers for their future happiness.

Such has been the patient sufferance of this society; and such is now the necessity which constrains them to alter their formerly adopted Technologies. The history of the present Big Bell Dogma is a history of repeated injuries and usurpations, all having in direct object the continuation of an absolute Tyranny over all people and businesses. To prove this, let Facts be submitted to a candid world.

- Limiting products so that they can only operate in a few fixed locations ("where they have always operated").

- Forcing services to only be offered in a constrained set of fixed locations ("where they have always been offered").

- Locking processes to only work in a relatively small number of places ("where they have always been performed").

- Forbidding (by law or policy) constituents from adopting otherwise viable and available mobile products, services, and technologies.

- Disabling or blocking technologies that otherwise would enable the power of mobility.

- Taxing or otherwise penalizing mobile products and services so as to destroy the financial value of adopting them.

- Charging mobile products, services, and technologies with pretended offenses so as to encourage fear, uncertainty, and doubt amongst those who otherwise would adopt and enjoy the power of mobility.

In every stage of these Oppressions We have proposed solutions in the most humble terms: Our repeated proposals have been answered only by repeated injury. A Dogma whose character is thus marked by every act which may define a Tyrant is unfit to define how we run our businesses, do our jobs, and live our lives.

Nor have We been wanting in warnings to our technology brethren. We have warned them from time to time of attempts by the Dogmatists to extend an unwarrantable jurisdiction over us. We have appealed to their native justice and magnanimity, and we have implored them by the ties of our common kindred to disavow these usurpations, which would inevitably interrupt our advances in productivity and connectivity. They too have been deaf to the voice of justice and of logic. We must, therefore, acquiesce in the necessity, and hold them, as we hold the rest of mankind, Enemies in War, in Peace Friends.

We, therefore, those seeking to drive mobility into all we do and are, appealing to the Supreme Judge of the world for the rectitude of our intentions, do, in the interest of serving this society and economy, solemnly publish and declare, That we are, and of Right ought to be Free and Mobile; that we are Absolved from all Allegiance to the Big Bell Dogma, and that all forced fixed connection is and ought to be totally dissolved; and that as a Free and Mobile Society, we have full Power to develop and implement mobile technologies, introduce new mobile processes, and to do all other Acts and Things which Free and Mobile businesses and individuals may of right do. And for the support of this Declaration, with a firm reliance on the protection of divine Providence, we mutually pledge to offer each other our Products, our Services, and our efficient Processes.

 **Case Study**

TeleNav

H. P. Jin had long envisioned that GPS technology would have a real impact on how people lived their lives and how businesses operated. Working as a consultant for McKinsey & Company and then at the McKenna Group, H. P. was able to see the seeds of this technology be planted at many companies around the globe. But the costs of implementation were too high and the challenges of broadly deploying GPS technology were too daunting for most companies to undertake.

However, H. P. recognized the opportunity for these challenges to be broadly overcome on September 15, 1999, when the Federal Communications Commission (FCC) revised its rules for wireless-enhanced 911 services. The original rules had been passed in 1996, requiring wireless carriers to be able to locate a wireless caller within 125 meters at least two thirds of the time by October 1, 2001. The 1999 rules change allowed carriers to accomplish this goal by embedding GPS technology into the wireless handset.[1]

Suddenly, it appeared that GPS technology would literally be placed in the hands of millions of consumers within a few years. H. P.

grabbed the opportunity, creating Televigation to focus on wireless telephone–based navigation products. The company would later shorten its name to TeleNav, Inc.

In 2000, the company introduced Snap-to-Map, a solution that didn't require GPS to be installed in the handset, but used the carrier's information about the user's location and the carrier's Wireless Application Protocol (WAP) services to provide turn-by-turn directions through a voice interface so the driver could keep his eyes on the road and his hands on the steering wheel. The service was trialed with two major carriers, proving the technical viability of the approach; however, the business models supported by the carriers could not support a profitable service for Televigation.

The company continued working with the major wireless carriers. One of these carriers, Nextel, offered an approach that was particularly well suited to Televigation's needs. Nextel standardized on a single Java-based platform for all of the phones they offered. Nextel was very supportive of developers and allowed Televigation to access the serial port on the phone to connect an external GPS receiver. In 2002, Televigation introduced a new product, TeleNav on Nextel phones, using a low-cost monthly subscription model. Later that year, Nextel introduced the industry's first handsets with GPS built in, enabling TeleNav to work without an external receiver so that only the cell phone was required. The product was well received by the market and was even named a *Time* magazine "Gadget of the Week."

By building the navigation function into a mobile phone, TeleNav overcame three obstacles that had limited the adoption and success of GPS-based technologies.

The first barrier was price. Stand-alone GPS units typically cost hundreds of dollars, creating a psychological barrier for consumers. Potential customers must be convinced that they will benefit from the technology before they will make an investment of that magnitude. TeleNav priced their product as a low monthly recurring fee. Today, customers can use TeleNav for about $10 per month and can cancel at any time, making it a much easier decision to try the technology.

How could TeleNav afford to disrupt the prevailing pricing model? By adding their product onto an existing customer handset, TeleNav leveraged the hardware investment that had already been made. Their competitors have to factor in the cost of all of the hardware components into their product cost and ensure that the up-front payment from the customer covers that hardware cost. TeleNav's approach also has ongoing support cost benefits. Software updates are automatically uploaded to the customers' handsets, eliminating the multistep process stand-alone units require, and maps are always up to date, reducing customer frustration and churn.

The second barrier that TeleNav's approach has overcome is availability. Customers who purchase a dedicated GPS unit typically install the unit in their car. However, if the customer isn't in that car, if they are in their other car, or riding with a friend, or once they leave their car and start walking, their big-ticket GPS system is no longer available to them. Because TeleNav's product is integrated into the customers' cell phones, the navigation feature is available wherever the phone goes, which means that it is available virtually 100% of the time.

Finally, because the TeleNav product is integrated into a phone, it has access to the network, so it overcomes the barrier of out-of-date information. The TeleNav product always benefits from the most recently available maps and has even been extended to provide up-to-date traffic, weather, and gas price information.

TeleNav has also worked with its carrier partners to integrate information on special events. For example, Sprint Nextel is the wireless partner to the NFL, so, working together, they integrated driving information for the 2007 SuperBowl into the TeleNav product.

So, what did it take for TeleNav to achieve this level of mobility success?

As a new company, TeleNav was free to play by the changing rules in the industry. They leveraged existing digital data and saw opportunity to differentiate by using the connectivity in the cell phone to provide updated information. They evaluated and understood the value they could create for their customers by integrating the power of mobility into their navigation product.

But none of that would have mattered if they had failed to execute.

According to H. P., the early partnership with Nextel was key to Televigation's success. By focusing their resources on one carrier that had the components necessary for the TeleNav product to succeed, the company was able to gain the greatest impact in the shortest time possible. As TeleNav has enjoyed success around the world, it has generally followed this same model, choosing one carrier that is well suited to the company's products in each market, focusing efforts at that one carrier, and enjoying outsized success with that carrier.

Now that TeleNav has established its success, and as other carriers have matured their platforms to support GPS-based solutions, the company has begun working with additional carriers.

"Wireless carriers are big companies that can be very slow to make decisions, but once they set a direction, they can move very fast. You need to align yourself with partners that are positioned to deliver what you need," counsels H. P. "And when they decide to move, you need to be lockstep with them, ready to move very fast."

TeleNav has moved very fast, first in lockstep with Nextel, then with Sprint Nextel, now with partners all over the world.

TELENAV'S MOBILIZED PRODUCTS

The following product descriptions are provided by TeleNav, Inc.

TeleNav offers two main product lines, TeleNav GPS Navigator and TeleNav Track.

TeleNav GPS Navigator is easy to use. As you drive, TeleNav will give you all the information you need, such as:

- The current street.
- The next turn to take.
- The next street to turn onto.
- The distance remaining before next turn.
- The number of miles left on your trip.

Along the way, turn-by-turn directions will be announced in a clear voice and displayed on your phone. For example, TeleNav will say, "Go 1.2 miles and turn right on Elm Street." As you approach the turn, you will hear, "Turn right on Elm Street."

TeleNav will even tell you whether the destination is on the left- or right-hand side of the street.

With TeleNav GPS Navigator, it is easy to find restaurants, banks, cafés, hotels, and more from over 10 million points of interest across the United States.

- Search by category, such as "Thai restaurant" and "pharmacy"
- Search by name, such as "Thai Basil" and "ABC Pharmacy"

Once you've found what you are looking for, you can use TeleNav to get turn-by-turn driving directions or call ahead to make reservations.

Best of all, updates are free and automatic, unlike expensive GPS systems that charge for updates and require manual intervention.

As you drive, TeleNav Traffic monitors the traffic situation every five minutes. When there is slowdown or incident, TeleNav Traffic proactively alerts you with a voice and onscreen prompt, "Accident 2.3 miles ahead on Main Street, one lane closed. Press '0' to avoid."

With just one click, TeleNav Traffic will intelligently reroute you to minimize travel time, taking into account the latest traffic conditions. Or you can continue on your course.

TeleNav even updates your estimated time of arrival (ETA), so you can set the proper expectations on when you will be there.

With TeleNav Track, you can manage your mobile workforce with confidence. TeleNav Track utilizes the latest technologies to make mobile workforce and asset management reliable and affordable for businesses of all sizes. Best of all, it works with your employees' mobile phones and personal digital assistants (PDAs).

You will be able to deploy mobile employees efficiently, allowing the most effective coverage of any area. You will even be able to predict arrival times and change schedules on the fly to better serve your customers.

TeleNav Track allows your mobile workforce to do their reporting from the road. No need returning to the office and filing invoices, orders, timesheets, and more. All data can be sent wirelessly.

With wireless bar code scanning, you will have an instant handle on deliveries, inventory, assets, and more. With that kind of real-time information, you will have the power to make quick, well-informed decisions.

TeleNav GPS Navigator^{TM} is incorporated into TeleNav Track and with turn-by-turn directions—onscreen and by voice—to lead them to their destinations, saving employees time and frustration.

Notes

1. www.constructionweblinks.com/Resources/Industry_Reports__ Newsletters/GPS_Nov_1999/gps_nov_1999.html.

CHAPTER 9

Limit

What Are You Going To Choose Not To Do?

Mobility is a wonderful thing. Obviously, this book is based on the assumption that mobility will be built into every product, service, and process. At the end of the day, well-defined standards and fully built-out reliable wireless networks will ensure that the infrastructure underlying mobility will work everywhere and all the time.

But we are not yet at the end of the day.

Different standards have taken hold in different parts of the world. Different network providers have selected different technologies that will work with their networks. Which provider's network works best varies from city to city, and even the best network in a city will have areas where performance is challenged.

You can't afford to wait for these issues to get resolved, so you had better figure out how to work within the current limitations to ensure that mobilizing your business does not destroy your brand, drive away customers, and kill your company.

There are four factors around which you should consider limiting the mobilization of your product, service, or process. These limitations will play out a bit differently for a product than for a service or a process, but the factors are the same:

- Wireless technology
- Network provider
- Geography
- Activities

As we will see, these four factors are all interrelated, so making the right choices will involve balancing the attractiveness of decisions in each area.

Wireless Technology

In most instances, mobilizing your product, service, or process will involve using wireless technologies. There is a broad array of technologies on the market, and new technologies being developed every year. Most of the technologies you will consider are international standards, meaning that you will have multiple vendors from which to choose in mobilizing your business.

The most meaningful way to characterize different technologies is in terms of their reach.

The shortest-reach technologies actually require wireless devices to touch or nearly touch each other to communicate. One standard in this space is near field communications (NFC) technology, jointly developed by Sony and Philips.[1] This technology can be used to pass information between two NFC-enabled devices. It is currently being targeted for inclusion in mobile phones for applications like the digital wallet (credit/debit transactions), identification, and electronic keys.

If NFC technology is broadly adopted and built into most mobile phones, it may be a valid choice for mobilizing your business. Obviously, its greatest limitation is that it requires the phone to come in close contact with another device. This may work if your employees or customers need to exchange information only when they return to a fixed location. It may also work in conjunction with a mobile NFC "reader" that is connected to the rest of the world using a different wireless technology.

A closely associated technology is radio frequency identification (RFID). RFID is being broadly adopted as the new standard for tagging items for retail, replacing the bar code system that became almost universally adopted during the PC revolution as inventory tracking and transaction processing were digitized. Because of this broad adoption, the cost of RFID tags is dropping rapidly (now as low as a few pennies each), making it a viable technology for a broad range of applications.

Passive RFID tags (those without a power source) are the smallest and least expensive and can operate up to a few meters.[2] Active tags are larger and more expensive, but can have ranges even into the hundreds of meters. An application of active RFID that you have probably encountered is the electronic toll pass, which identifies cars passing through a toll plaza allowing them to automatically pay without slowing or stopping.

The greatest limitation with RFID is that it is primarily designed for identification purposes. It is not a two-way networking protocol, and the amount of data that can be transmitted is intended to be small.

RFID may be part of a mobilization strategy, but is not likely to enable true mobilization of products, services, or processes.

The next class of wireless technologies is known as personal area networks (PANs). PANs are designed to connect multiple electronic devices together, generally for use by one person and in very close proximity. Wireless PAN technologies include Bluetooth and ZigBee.

Bluetooth has been broadly adopted for consumer electronics applications such as cordless telephone headsets, printer connections, and remote control and input devices. It can work up to about 100 meters and is designed for simple setup (which limits sophisticated features such as advanced security).

ZigBee is intended to be even simpler than Bluetooth, which contributes to a lower cost (currently in the neighborhood of $1 per device).[3] ZigBee nodes automatically form mesh networks to cover a larger area than would otherwise be associated with a PAN. Typical ZigBee applications include networks for industrial sensors, home automation, and alarm monitoring.

PAN technologies can be a great tool in mobilizing products, services, and processes, but primarily in connecting together different parts of the solution. For example, Bluetooth can be used to pass data between different components, such as to connect an RFID reader to the main data collection and networking node. ZigBee and Bluetooth generally are less useful for connecting together products or employees on a broader scale.

The next class of technology is local area networking (LAN). The most prevalent wireless LAN technology today is known as WiFi. WiFi technologies provide multi-megabit transmissions over hundreds of meters. Mesh networks are also being built out of hundreds of WiFi access points to cover entire cities. WiFi is a general computer networking technology that is well suited to carrying Internet-like data traffic and is beginning to be used for performance-sensitive applications like voice calls and multiplayer gaming.

WiFi's greatest limitations come from signal coverage and quality challenges. Users can experience challenges with signal strength variations due to a variety of factors including interference, contention from other users, and propagation through walls. WiFi is a relatively mature technology with strong tools for managing the network, including security authentication and encryption.

Using a WiFi network dedicated to mobilizing a service or process and managing that network to provide the needed performance in the area where the service is provided or the process is performed can prove highly effective. However, extending that service or process beyond the controlled area becomes a challenge.

Using WiFi to integrate mobility into a product is also worth considering. Many technology-oriented consumers have implemented WiFi networks in their homes, and WiFi has also been broadly adopted by businesses. However, security concerns have caused consumers and businesses to wisely deploy standard authentication schemes that will require the product to be configured to interact with specific secure WiFi networks, adding to the complexity of the product and likely inhibiting full use of the mobilized features. Since it will be impossible for you to ensure the quality of the network where your product is used, you will need to ensure that the product performs acceptably when the network signal is poor or even nonexistent. This could significantly limit the extent to which you can claim the increased value of your product due to mobility.

The final class of wireless technologies is the wide area network (WAN). Third-generation wireless wide area networking technologies that are broadly deployed globally include high-speed packet access (HSPA) technologies and CDMA2000 (code division multiple access) technologies such as EV-DO (evolution data optimized). These technologies are used by licensed cellular telephone companies to provide data services covering entire cities, regions, or countries. Currently, these services offer speeds in the 1-Mbps range and can work even when traveling at highway speeds.

Fourth-generation wireless WAN technologies are now emerging that provide multi-megabit data rates at highway speeds. The leading international standard is WiMax, which can provide up to 40 Mbps per channel at a cost point that is dramatically lower than existing wireless WAN technologies.[4] Sprint Nextel is currently deploying a nationwide WiMax network.

Wireless WAN technologies are well suited to mobilizing products, services, and processes. As with mobile phones today, there will be pockets of coverage challenges in any wireless network, but in general, wireless WANs provide significantly greater reach providing a much higher confidence that a signal will be present where the product is being used, the service is being provided, or the process is being performed.

Third-generation wireless WAN technologies generally require advance activation by the carrier, which can add a slight barrier to product mobility adoption. Pricing plans for third-generation offers may also inhibit broad use as a mobility value-add for products (many carriers charge based on usage, and pricing plans are typically $15 per month or more). However, these challenges are much less of an issue when mobilizing a service or a process.

Sprint Nextel's fourth-generation WiMax network is specifically being designed for integration into mobilized products. Instant, automated, over-the-air activation and pricing plans better suited to mobilized products are currently being developed. Fourth-generation technologies will also support mobilized services and processes with higher performance, perhaps even at lower costs. Intel is a strong supporter of the WiMax standards and has indicated that they will push for WiMax capabilities to be embedded into all computing products, just as virtually all laptops sold today include WiFi networking.

It is not economical to build all of these wireless technologies into your product, service, or process, so one of the first decisions you'll need to make is which technologies will best meet your goals and how that will drive additional limitations for your business.

Network Provider

Based on the wireless technologies you choose to build mobility into your product, service, or process, you will need to determine whether to build and operate your own wireless network or whether to partner with a network provider.

NFC, RFID, and PANs will almost always need to be implemented to your unique specifications. Although it may be wise to outsource the building and operating of the network, your opportunity to share the cost with other companies is limited. Still, an experienced partner can bring best practices to bear in deploying your network quickly and cost effectively and likely can centralize operations into their existing network operations centers.

Selecting an outsource partner likely will be based on a variety of factors, including your previous experience or recommendations of those you trust and a bid that appears competitive relative to others you consider. However, most important will be a partner's proven expertise supporting the technologies you've selected and how you plan on using the network. As you negotiate with your partner, keep in mind that the choices you make now may limit how quickly you can expand your mobilization efforts into new areas. A provider with proven success supporting your immediate needs and a broad portfolio of additional capabilities may enable you to rapidly build on your early mobility successes.

If you have selected wireless LAN technologies, the range of network providers available to support you broadens. If you plan on primarily using WiFi technologies in the locations that you control, then the best approach may again be to find an outsource partner to build and operate the network. If you are interested in opening this WiFi network up for your customers to use, it would be wise to look for a partner with specific expertise in this area. You will need to ensure that your partner has proven experience protecting your network and all the data on it from the general public.

However, if you hope to use public WiFi networks as your customers and/or employees travel around the world, then you should look for a network provider who has roaming agreements providing connectivity in thousands of locations. T-Mobile provides WiFi connectivity to its customers in about 30,000 locations in 22 countries. Sprint customers can use their WiFi service in over 20,000 locations around the world. Boingo, a WiFi-only network provider, offers connectivity in 60,000 locations in about 75 countries.

Again, you should choose a provider not just based on your current plans, but taking into account its ability to support you as you expand your mobilization efforts to additional technologies and applications.

Wireless WAN technologies provide the most straightforward choices and the most apparent sets of limitations. Depending on the wireless WAN technology that best serves your needs, there will be a clear set of carriers supporting that technology. For example, in the United States, AT&T currently supports the HSPA 3G technology family, and T-Mobile is beginning to build their network to support the HSPA standards. Verizon supports the CDMA2000 standards, as does Sprint, while Sprint is also building out a WiMax 4G network. In part, selecting a network partner is as simple as identifying which carriers support your current and future network technology needs.

Another limiting factor in choosing a wireless WAN provider is the device technologies that they support. If you are building a product that will be integrated into the handsets offered by a wireless carrier, then you will need to consider the openness of the carrier to your development efforts. You will need to consider the technologies built into their handsets. Do they support the operating environment that best suits your needs and skills? Do their handsets include the contextual sources (e.g., GPS) and support any peripheral devices (e.g., RFID readers, environmental sensors) that are required for your solution?

If you are going to build the wireless WAN technology into your product, does the carrier actively support embedded solutions? How robust are their support services? Will you be able to test your product sufficiently on their network? Do they see partners like you as an opportunity or a threat?

If you are mobilizing a service or process, are the applications already available to support your employees using the devices they offer for their network? How mature are their processes and organizations in supporting business mobilization efforts? Do they have experience working with an organization like yours on an application like this, or will you be providing them with a "learning opportunity" that may not go well for you?

There are also very well defined geographic limitations imposed by selecting a network provider for wireless WAN services. T-Mobile is owned by Deutsche Telekom, and therefore has some connection to European services, but in general, selecting a network provider in the United States will solve only your U.S. connectivity needs. If you need connectivity in different parts of the world, you will generally need to select different partners in each region or country.

Because of this complexity, it will likely make sense to limit your initial mobilization efforts to a single country with a single network provider and consider expanding as your experience and support resources allow.

Geography

This takes us directly to geographic limitations.

If the mobilization of your product, service, or process involves working with a wireless WAN network provider, then you will naturally want to limit the geographic reach of your solution to match the footprint of your partner. In the United States, the national carriers have extended their networks through builds and partnerships to cover virtually all of the reasonably populated areas of the country. But, as noted above, their networks do not extend beyond the borders of the country.

Wireless LAN, PAN, RFID, and NFC wireless technologies create even more significant limitations on the geographic reach of your solution.

As previously discussed, PAN, RFID, and NFC solutions will require a dedicated infrastructure, so you will need to limit the mobility of your solutions based on where you are willing and able to build out that infrastructure. You may allow your employees or customers to wander beyond that geography to perform tasks, but they will need to return to reconnect and gain the full benefit of mobility.

Wireless LAN technologies promise much greater mobility, but the real-world experiences of your customers and employees may make it challenging for you to capture the value of mobility if relying on these technologies to provide significant geographic reach. In theory, WiFi hotspots are available all over the world, including public networks, networks to which you can subscribe for access, and private (business and residential) networks that your customers or employees may be able to authenticate to. However, the coverage area of this vast array of hundreds of thousands of hotspots is just a small fraction of the area covered by wireless WAN technologies, and the performance experienced by users may vary dramatically.

Since you have almost no control over this virtual cloud of WiFi coverage, either directly or through well-established network provider relationships, your ability to influence or even monitor what your customers and employees are experiencing is virtually nonexistent. The net result may be a failure to adopt the mobility solutions in which you've invested, thus eliminating your opportunity to capture the value that should accrue from mobility.

For these reasons, especially in the earliest days of your mobilization efforts, it would be best to limit the geography over which you implement your solution to a footprint over which you either have direct control or your network providers are willing to guarantee performance through service-level agreements.

Activities

The geographic limitations you have selected for the mobilization of your product, service, or process likely will lead to natural limitations in the activities that are fully mobilized using wireless technologies.

For a mobilized product, this may dictate the features that you will support in the early releases of your industry-defining offers. As you gain experience and confidence enabling you to extend the geographic reach, you may find that additional features may be supportable. For example, if your initial product release relies on WiFi networking, you may store enough data within the product for it to work reasonably well even when a live connection is not available. The synchronization of data can occur whenever a WiFi connection can be obtained. However, once your product is upgraded to include WiMax network technologies, and as WiMax network coverage gets expanded, your confidence that a connection will almost always be available will enable you to include live information and even real-time communications in your product features.

Similarly for service and process mobilization efforts, if you've chosen WiFi as your networking technology, then you will limit the mobilized activities that can occur within the footprint of the infra-structure you have built and can manage. However, if you have selected wireless WAN technologies, then you can mobilize activities that can be performed virtually anywhere there are people (cities, towns, highways).

Remember, the goal is to increase the value of your product, service, or process through mobility. That value creation comes from increased availability of the product or service and its contextual relevance. The opportunities for contextual relevance are almost limitless as location information (from GPS receivers), environmental information (from a variety of sensors), health information (from medical telemetry devices), time and date (from various time sources), and a variety of network sources of data can all be built into your product. However, the choices you make about wireless networking technologies and providers will have a direct impact on how limited (or not) the availability gains are that you are introducing.

To ensure that your mobilization efforts create value by increasing availability and contextual relevance rather than destroy value by failing to work where and when your customer or employee expects, it is critical that you appropriately limit the geographic reach and activities/functions to match the choices you have made in network technologies and provider.

And these limitations will likely lead directly to your selection of target markets, customers, and applications.

 FROM THE REAL WORLD

When Less Is Best

Sometimes even wireless carriers need to narrow their focus to maximize success.

When Sprint Nextel introduced Advanced Wireless Solutions in 2006, it was already the market share leader in wireless solutions for businesses. The company had the broadest portfolio of available solutions, with dozens of products meeting the diverse needs of functional groups across several industry vertical markets.

But, in fact, all that choice wasn't making life easier for Sprint's customers. As businesses recognized building mobility into their processes and services was becoming a competitive imperative, actually figuring out what they needed and how to implement it became daunting. Sprint's Advanced Wireless Solutions were designed to dramatically simplify the decision process and accelerate the implementation of mobility for these businesses.

Paul Deering, vice president of Advanced Wireless Solutions recognized that fewer was better. "By initially focusing on just the six challenges that are best solved with mobility solutions today, and then picking a short list of partners that consistently deliver the best results, we have amplified our impact many times over."

By limiting the number of mobility solutions, Sprint has developed deep expertise in those solutions and tight relationships with the software partners. This allows Sprint to tightly integrate the applications into its core operations, thoroughly test the solution with its chosen handsets across its network, and focus all of its resources on delivering a great experience for six right solutions.

Sprint's customers directly enjoy the benefits of this focus. Not only is the selection process simplified, Sprint has used its broad experience to pick the best software and the best handsets running over its powerful networks, but the application of that solution to the customer's unique needs is well served by Sprint's deep knowledge and close partnering for this select group of solutions.

By choosing to do a few things very well, Paul's team can also deliver an exceptional implementation and ongoing support experience that is critical to Sprint customers fully capturing the power of mobility.

 **Case Study**

Sport Clips

I am not a big fan of getting my hair cut.

Having a stylish "do" is not high on my list of priorities (if you have seen me, it shows).

Getting my hair cut takes time, especially since I prefer the types of salons where you don't need an appointment and the value proposition is all about a decent cut at a low price. Sitting and waiting for my turn while flipping through some entertainment magazine looking for something interesting to pass the time is downright painful.

And then, finally, I get in the chair and the stylist wants to talk to me about my day. What's the deal? And what's that smelly stuff you're putting in my hair?

Thank goodness for the Sport Clips concept. Sport Clips provides high-quality haircuts in a fun sports environment, complete with TVs at every stylist's station tuned to sports. Every Sport Clips has "guy smart" stylists who focus on providing the highest level of service to every client.

Apparently, the concept resonates with more guys than just me. Sport Clips is one of America's fastest-growing franchises, with more than 400 locations in 33 states, and that number is doubling every year. In fact, one franchisee is planning on building 30 new Sport Clips stores in Las Vegas alone.[5]

However, since guys like me don't really care about our hair, Sports Clips will grow only if my experience is positive instead of painful so I will be willing to go out of my way and pay a little bit more for that experience. Each shop's business will grow or decline based on how well they manage that positive experience, but what I tell my buddies will also impact the brand and growth of the overall franchise.

"Our job is to ensure that guys that come into a Sport Clips store will get a quality haircut and have a great experience," notes Kerin Haney, vice president of field operations for Sport Clips.

The national Sport Clips brand stands for something, and poor performance by local stores can undermine that brand and quickly destroy the growth potential of the overall business.

Sport Clips clearly understands this dynamic and manages it closely. The company has 60 field district managers and coaches who regularly visit each shop to provide coaching and to ensure that franchise standards are being met so that clients' experiences support the brand. These field managers complete a lengthy site survey during each visit. Historically, this process has been paper based, with the field personnel mailing in completed survey forms.

As the company was evaluating options for equipping the field force with updated wireless devices, the timing seemed perfect to consider setting the new standard for franchise brand management by mobilizing the entire site survey process.

"Believe it or not, word of mouth moves even faster than we're growing," observes Clete Brewer, Sport Clips president. "When our folks in the field uncover a problem, we need to move quickly to resolve it."

Case Study (continued)

Sport Clips worked with Anyware Mobile Solutions to transform their paper-based process into a paperless application running on Palm Treo smart devices connected back to Anyware over the Sprint Nextel mobile broadband network. Anyware collects and compiles the data input by the field technicians and immediately sends out alert notifications via e-mail to key Sport Clips personnel.

As field managers move through the different stations within each store, they click off results of the survey. As soon as they are done, any combination of factors that indicate a problem is flagged for that field manager and reported back to headquarters. The field personnel can immediately begin working with the local "team leader" (the franchisee) to develop an action plan to resolve the issues.

The survey results are also captured in the Anyware database and are used to produce historical trend results on key metrics that can help identify developing issues before they can become significant problems that could damage the brand. Sport Clips has also been able to use this data to identify differences between stores and to translate those differences into standard best practices that can benefit all team leaders.

In addition to the immediacy of the reporting, Sport Clips has also benefited from the improved accuracy and efficiency that comes from not having to key in data at headquarters that has been collected on paper in the field. Field personnel can also attach electronic files, and all of the information gets integrated into the company's customer relationship management (CRM) system, enabling a much richer and timelier view of each franchisee and location.

As with any championship team, excellent execution and clear communication are keys to gaining a competitive advantage. The combination of Treo smart devices, mobile e-mail, and the mobilized site survey application have Sport Clips operating at the top of their game.

"Every entrepreneur has a choice," Clete notes. "Our franchisees have bet their life on our brand. By mobilizing our field interactions, we've dramatically increased the odds of that bet paying off for our franchise partners."

But mobilization has been a big bet for Sport Clips as well. To increase their odds, the company standardized on one device on one network, and they turned to an expert who has worked extensively with those technologies. Outsourcing the collection, tabulation, and reporting functions further simplified the overall deployment and increased the likelihood of success.

Of course, Clete clearly understands this model: "The great thing about the franchise model is that our franchisees can focus on a small set of decisions. They trust us to be experts in everything else, empowering them to succeed in running their business. It's been the same way with Sprint and Anyware. We know they're the experts and that they've spent years getting the devices, network, and application model working well together. We just need to focus on making our business a success."

And from the looks of it, Clete and team are hitting the ball out of the park!

Notes

1. http://en.wikipedia.org/wiki/Near_Field_Communication.

2. http://en.wikipedia.org/wiki/Rfid.

3. http://en.wikipedia.org/wiki/Zigbee.

4. http://www.wimaxforum.org/technology.

5. www.sportclips.com/about_us/press_box/pr201.asp. "A Cut Above the Rest," February 16, 2007, Las Vegas Business Press, Staff Report.

CHAPTER 10

Position
Select Your Target Markets, Customers, and Applications

Building mobility into your product, service, or process requires investment and introduces change for your employees and customers. That change may be embraced, or it may be rejected. Because of this uncertainty, and to limit your initial investment, it's wise to carefully select a limited initial deployment to gain experience, fine tune the mobile integration, and prove the business case for maximum success with minimum pain moving forward.

For these reasons, in selecting the initial target markets, customers, and applications for your move into mobility, it is critical to think in terms of three factors:

1. Risk
2. Reward
3. Replication

Risk

The old saying is "with the greater the risk, comes the greater reward," but we all know that's not always accurate. Great rewards are rarely gained without any risk, but a wise businessman will find ways to eliminate unnecessary risk and balance the necessary risk with the available rewards.

When mobilizing a product, service, or process, risk takes three primary forms. The most obvious is the risk that things just won't work when your customers and employees expect them to. We'll call this *performance risk*. The second very scary risk is that your mobilized product, service, or process will work perfectly, but your customers and employees will reject it. We'll call this *acceptance risk*. The third kind of risk is the best kind of all—*success risk*. Success risk represents the chance that your customers and employees will so strongly embrace your mobilized product, service, or process that they will demand that it expand where it works and what it encompasses faster than you can keep up, leading to frustration for them and stress on your operations for you.

Since eliminating these risks is likely impossible, the key is to evaluate them up front, making key decisions to limit the likelihood or impact of each type of risk, and actively monitoring and managing your mobility introduction to respond well if the risks become reality.

Let's start with performance risk. Carefully evaluate the potential sources of failure that can cause your newly mobilized product, service, or process to fail. The most obvious sources of failure will be any newly introduced components.

Are you adding in new pieces of hardware? How reliable are these components? Are there conditions under which they are more likely to fail than others? Is a component susceptible to failure from interference or weather conditions or long periods of continuous use? How difficult, expensive, and time consuming is it to replace a failed component? In choosing your initial implementation, what choices can you make to limit the likelihood of failure of each new hardware component? What choices can you make to accelerate and minimize the cost of fixing any failures? What choices can you make to minimize the impact on your customers and employees if there is a failure? Can you choose specific applications for specific target customers/employees in specific geographies that will both reduce the likelihood of failure of your new hardware components and minimize the impact of any such failure?

Are there software components in your new mobilized implementation? Is it possible to allow frequent updates of the software to fix diagnosed problems with minimal impact to the users? Can you choose specific applications for specific target customers/employees in specific geographies that will reduce the impact of software failures and increase the opportunity for painless software upgrades?

Are you reliant on communications networks as you mobilize your product, service, or process? Where do those networks operate most reliably? Under what conditions are they likely to fail? How well does your product, service, or process work if the network isn't working? For how long can it continue to be valuable between successful network connections? Will network failures be more noticeable and frustrating for different types of customers or employees? What decisions can you make to minimize the risk and impact of network failures? Can you use local data storage to ensure that your product, service, or process will still be valuable even when the network isn't working? Can you limit the geographies for your product, service, or process to increase the likelihood that the network will be available and reliable? Are there applications that are better suited to use local data storage when the network is down, but that will still benefit from mobilization when the network is active? Can you select target customers or employees who will be best suited to the anticipated reliability of the network?

Acceptance risk is much less scientifically managed than performance risk. Understanding how people will perform is inherently more challenging than understanding how hardware, software, and networks will perform.

Acceptance risk is best managed by carefully selecting initial target customers or employees, communicating with them well in advance of the coming changes, providing sufficient training for them to rapidly gain the benefits of mobility, and providing effective and timely support when they do encounter uncertainty or problems.

Consider the combination of hardware, software, and networking that you're introducing as you mobilize your product, service, or process. Are there target customers or employees who are already comfortable with these technologies or who have previously demonstrated openness to advances in these directions? Are there users who have proven willing to work with you in introducing new technologies and are therefore both willing and able to adapt, even through early performance challenges?

Are there target users, applications, or geographies that are better suited to the communications, training, and support tasks required to ensure successful acceptance and adoption? Is there a subset of potential users that are located where face-to-face communications, training, and support can easily and cost effectively be provided, increasing likely success? Are there target applications that would simplify the communications, training, and support efforts? By limiting the geographic reach of the mobilized product, service, or process, can you significantly increase your ability to provide timely and effective support to quickly resolve issues and concerns and increase the likelihood of acceptance?

Success risk shouldn't be shrugged off with an offhand statement like "That will be a good problem to have." Success risk must be carefully considered from the beginning and managed just as actively as other risks to your mobility implementation.

There are two fundamental approaches to managing success risk. The first is to be prepared to scale up when success hits and demand outpaces current capabilities. The second is to select initial implementations with dimensions of expansion that reduce the scale of expansion required.

Demand for expansion can come in any of several dimensions. Current users may desire that you expand the value of mobility into an increasing range of capabilities, products, services, or processes. They may desire that the mobilization work in a broader geography. Or additional customers or employees may demand that they have access to the successfully mobilized product, service, or process. And these new users may require slightly different applications in different geographies than your original target.

What would it take for you to scale in each of these dimensions? What preparation can you take to be prepared to quickly expand each dimension? Are their choices you can make in the technologies, components, and networks used in mobilizing your product, service, or process that would make it easier to scale up? When choosing suppliers, which suppliers are best prepared to support your potential future expansion? What can you do to prepare for potential expansion in manufacturing or support? What impact will potential geographic expansion have on your technology, component, network, supplier, manufacturing, and support decisions?

Once you understand what it takes to be prepared to scale in each of these dimensions, and which you can afford to put in place advanced preparation, you're better prepared to evaluate which initial target customers or employees, geographies, and applications expose you to the greatest likelihood to expand in areas where you are least prepared to scale. Can you choose initial users who have limited additional uses into which they will ask you to expand, or who have limited geographies they will expect you to cover? Which initial users and applications can limit the appeal to additional users who you are best positioned to expand to serve?

Taking into account each form of risk—performance risk, acceptance risk, and success risk—you should be able to develop a clear picture of the portfolio of risks as they associate to the potential target customers or employees, applications, and geographies that you could initially target with your newly mobilized product, service, or process.

Reward

Identifying the best target users, applications, and geographies shouldn't just be about managing risk. You must also consider the potential reward associated with these choices.

Your reward will likely take the form of some combination of profitability, share of decisions, and loyalty. For mobilized products and services, these rewards specifically are premium pricing, market share, and customer lifetime value. If your mobilization involves a service or process, profitability may also come from reduced operating costs, and share of decisions may include your attractiveness to potential employees, and loyalty extends to employee loyalty, yielding a variety of benefits to your business.

Within the context of managing performance, acceptance, and success risks, your choices for target customers, applications, and geographies will be selected based on opportunities to maximize market share, profitability, customer loyalty, employee attractiveness, and employee loyalty.

In choosing to maximize these rewards, you likely will consider the opportunity to clearly differentiate your product or service from competitors through mobilization, leading to the opportunity for premium pricing, to take market share, and to gain customer loyalty. You likely will also consider the opportunity to reduce costs, increasing profitability. Finally, you will also consider whether your new mobilized products, services, or processes appeal to your current and prospective employees, making it easier to hire and retain the talent you need for your business to be successful.

To fully maximize the rewards of your mobilization initiatives, you will want to achieve all of these benefits on the largest scale possible, supporting the largest possible collection of customers and employees with the broadest possible array of applications, across the most expansive geographic reach.

However, that, of course, flies in the face of managing the risk. Therefore, the right choices will balance the desire to maximize the reward while minimizing the associated risks.

Replication

Both of these desires, reducing initial risk and maximizing the reward, are well served by making choices that enable rapid replication.

Can you choose an initial set of customers or employees for your mobilization efforts that are well suited as a model for a much broader base, so once the implementation is reliable and supportable, it can quickly be expanded to many others?

Can you choose an initial geography that involves a set of regulatory, market, and technology conditions that make an excellent blueprint for replicating the implementation over time to new geographies? This may mean designing for the worst geographic environment and then knowing that "if it works here, it will work anywhere." Or it may mean designing for a cutting-edge environment that is setting the standards that the rest of the world is likely to follow. Both approaches are valid, but each obviously represents different timing and different levels of capability.

Can you choose an initial set of applications that can serve as a prototype from which many additional applications can quickly be supported by making relatively minor adjustments to the initial implementation? Is there a base application on which many other applications can be layered?

Wrapping It All Together

Taking all of these factors together, the key decisions you will make in your initial mobilization efforts include choosing which users (customers or employees) to initially target, for which applications of your product, service, or process, and in which geographies.

The right answer will depend somewhat on your tolerance for risk, but will be the combination that both minimizes your risks around performance and acceptance and that positions you to rapidly replicate your success to maximize the rewards that you reap.

Mobility creates tremendous opportunity to win in your industry by increasing your market share, increasing your profitability, and attracting and retaining the best talent. But, if you stumble with your first mobilization efforts in the wrong place in front of the wrong customers and employees in a way that is devastating to how they value your company, then your mobilization efforts will destroy value rather than create it.

Choose well!

 FROM THE REAL WORLD

Laying a Firm Foundation

One of my side activities is work I do with Living Stones Ministry (www.lstones.com). Living Stones provides software building blocks that churches and other ministries can use to make their Web sites more dynamic and interactive.

Unlike most of the entities featured in this book, Living Stones had neither an existing base of organizations it was serving nor an existing set of services that it was offering. As a start-up ministry, it had the freedom to choose any offers to first bring to "market" and it did not have a base to "sell" into. The ministry could choose virtually any starting point—any target "market" and any initial set of applications—and grow from there.

Although the technologies that Living Stones is working with are not specifically mobility-centric, the thought processes, and the balancing of risk, reward, and replication are very similar to what you may face as you consider mobilizing your products, services, and processes.

Living Stones' model is to provide a software building block that provides a specific dynamic and interactive capability that can immediately create incremental value for a church's existing Web site. Living Stones faced the exact same three risks described in this chapter: performance risk, acceptance risk, and success risk.

Software products seem to attract bugs. Therefore, our expectation was that the software would face performance challenges. Our hope was that we would work through the most significant problems quickly with the first few "customers." From the beginning, we structured the product so that new versions could easily be downloaded and installed without a lot of reintegration required. However, we are currently on our third model for distribution. The first made it too difficult to notify users that a new version of software was available. The second required too much up-front registration work so it became a barrier to adoption. We're hoping we finally have found a balance between the two. In establishing the overall architecture, we knew that we needed to be prepared to fix performance problems in a way that would scale rapidly if we experienced tremendous success. This isn't any easier than it sounds, but we still believe it's essential to our ability to truly make an impact.

Acceptance risk has become a multiheaded beast that we haven't yet conquered. We made a number of up-front choices specifically to ease the adoption of the Living Stones software. We chose to use technologies that would be supported on the vast majority of Web hosting platforms that churches are likely to already be using, so technology isn't an issue. We chose to create a new open-source styled license with no licensing fees, so price isn't a barrier to adoption. We put intense focus into truly creating "building blocks" that are easy to add to an existing Web site so that complexity wouldn't become a barrier to adoption. All of those decisions have been essential to reducing the acceptance risk.

However, we've found that our current offers still require some knowledge of how to edit the files on the Web server and how to access a database system. For most church administrators, this is scary stuff! The folks who have been willing to try the Living Stones software have proven to be technically competent individuals. Unfortunately, most technically competent folks aren't necessarily attracted to the simplicity and "building block" model represented by Living Stones offers. Many of them would rather struggle through trying to build the same capabilities themselves than drop in a building block we've provided. Obviously, there are plenty of churches that have technically competent Web support folks who are happy to implement what we've provided, but needing to find that "middle ground" market has been an acceptance risk that we hadn't originally anticipated.

We managed the success risk from the beginning by building the product for easy replication. As a zero-income nonprofit, we've had to ensure automation and plug-and-play success to create any meaningful value.

The reward equation is dramatically different for a nonprofit than it is for a corporation. Our reward is not measured in profitability, but we do hope that many churches and ministries will choose our solution and will continue to use and derive value from it for years to come.

The two key decisions we made early in the start-up of Living Stones were to pick two key applications we would initially deliver and to pick one church that we would work closely with as a "beta-test" customer to refine the product and our processes.

FROM THE REAL WORLD (CONTINUED)

The two applications we targeted were a Bible interface and a sermon database. Christian churches base their authority and their ministry on the Bible, so it is only natural for a church Web site to include the ability to read and search the scriptures. However, from our personal experience, we knew that it was very difficult to add this functionality to a church Web site. In short, there was almost universal pent-up demand for this capability on church Web sites.

Similarly, most churches have a desire to enable their sermon content to have an impact beyond the half hour it is heard in the church sanctuary and even beyond the life impact it has on those sitting in the pews that Sunday morning. A growing number of churches have figured out how to add sermon notes and audio files to their Web sites, but it's generally not easy and it's even harder to maintain these files over time. Therefore, we believed that these two applications would provide nearly universal appeal, enabling us to have the greatest impact as church after church replicates these applications into their Web sites. These choices have proven to be well directed.

In choosing a single church to start with as a "beta" site, we wanted one that placed high value on the capabilities of their Web site, that especially valued our two target applications, that had the right technical capabilities to make it work, and that was open to implementing something new like Living Stones. It turns out that my local church, Oak Hills Presbyterian (www.oakhillspca.com) was a perfect candidate. The original Web site design by Toby Becker and John Burke was both progressive and based on the same technologies Living Stones relied on, so adding in the Living Stones building blocks did not encounter any acceptance barriers. The two pastors, Russ Ramsey and Jon Dunning, are both young men with a strong appreciation for modern technology, so they both embraced the new Bible and sermon capabilities, but also became active supporters of Living Stones, providing exactly the kind of input and feedback necessary of a beta customer.

In the case of Living Stones, with zero advertising budget, that first customer also became the marketing platform—using it as a visible example when approaching other churches to serve and reaching out to others through the personal network of pastors that Russ and Jon had developed.

In short, those early decisions have proven foundational to the ongoing success of Living Stones Ministry.

Case Study

Montclair State University

Have you heard of Montclair State University? Many haven't yet, but it is New Jersey's second largest university with over 16,000 students on a 246-acre campus just 14 miles from New York City.

The school, like many universities today, was facing a widening communications challenge. Today's students are more connected than any previous generation. A typical freshman shows up with a cell phone he's had for years, a Web mail address all of his friends have memorized, and instant message and text message accounts that keep his fingers flying almost nonstop throughout the day.

In other words, most students have fully embraced mobile communications and need no help from the university in getting reconnected. Although the university provides telephones in the residence halls and e-mail accounts for all students, the kids would rather use the cell phones and Web mail accounts they know and love. They rarely use the dorm phones and don't bother checking their school e-mail accounts.

So, although today's students are more connected than ever before, they are shunning the communications channels provided by the university and on which schools have relied in getting critical information out to students. Short of showing up at a student's dorm room at 7 A.M., there's no way to ensure that a student receives critical academic, community, or emergency information.

Since universities are always resource constrained, spending budget dollars and staff time to maintain a phone system that students won't use proves increasingly hard to justify.

To overcome these challenges, Montclair State University turned to Sprint Nextel and Rave Wireless to implement an innovative wireless solution that perfectly fits students' lifestyles, addresses the school's communications and budget challenges, and greatly enhances the University's ability to engage its students and improve their living and learning experience.

"Communications are at the center of any modern university," notes Dr. Susan A. Cole, president of Montclair State University. "Students are used to universities being one step behind them. With our Campus Connect mobile phone program, we're one step ahead of them and it's created an interesting cultural shift."

Typically, universities feature grand buildings built to serve generations of students. These robust structures weren't built with wireless signal penetration in mind. Therefore, campuses are plagued with coverage dead spots, often in the areas where communications could be most valuable. As students have increasingly adopted mobile phones as their primary communications tool, universities, like Montclair State, have found the need to partner with a carrier to ensure excellent coverage everywhere and to better connect faculty and staff to the students using wireless technologies. Frost & Sullivan estimates that university spending on wireless voice and data services will more than double between 2006 and 2009.[1]

Sprint Nextel has built out the wireless infrastructure on the Montclair State campus to ensure that students always have reliable coverage. Students use Sprint Nextel phones and service even as they leave campus and travel home to their families. Montclair designed the program to provide the commuter population with a virtual on-campus experience through the Campus Connect device. The Sprint Nextel solution also provides the unified messaging platform that the university needed. Depending on the urgency of the message, university officials can immediately communicate with everyone on campus via text message, e-mail, and/ or voice mail.

Dr. Karen L. Pennington, vice president for student development and campus life, observes, "the quality of the student's experience is extremely important. Students who are happy and connected to an institution are integrated into the environment. After many years of research, we know that those are the students who do well academically and succeed better socially. Campuses that have students who connect, they connect not just in the short term, but they connect in the long term; they connect as alumni which helps improve alumni giving."

The biggest challenge is truly connecting. Students show up with a cellphone in their pocket. Why would they change to a phone provided by the school? Without broad student adoption, Montclair State University would never achieve its objectives. Three keys to driving adoption at Montclair State have been number portability so students can stay in touch with their friends, the excellent wireless coverage across the entire campus, and the suite of mobile applications and content provided by Sprint Nextel and Rave Wireless.

"We decided to launch the mobile phone program at Montclair State to actually create a situation for students to become much more engaged with their peers and with the faculty and have ready access to the various services we provide," recalls Dr. Edward Chapel, chief information officer, Montclair State University. "Choosing the small number of applications that have fully engaged students into the virtual and on-campus experience has been critical to student acceptance and even enthusiasm."

Students love many of the applications that are available to all customers on Sprint Nextel's network. Push-to-talk is a great fit with the campus lifestyle, and the opportunity to customize the phone with features like hip ring tones goes a long way toward making students comfortable moving to a new device. Additionally, Rave has created a suite of applications specific to the campus environment.

Dr. Chapel's team surveyed students to identify the applications of greatest interest to students. They initially launched a trial involving 200 users (students and faculty) to prove the value of the solution. And the university and its partners have been very responsive to new requests and ideas from students. The most heavily used applications to date are the BlackBoard Course Management Service and applications that provide basic community-building features such as a student directory integrated with the phone's calling, texting, and e-mailing features, user-generated content publishing, and group management.

The cell phone then moves into the classroom. Montclair State University wireless users can tap straight into the course management software that drives the university's academic programs. Instructors can also easily communicate with students and even use phones for in-class polling. A wide array of campus information, from class schedules to dining hall menus to shuttle bus schedules are all available to students through their phones.

But the two applications that have really driven broad adoption are the shuttle bus tracker and the Mobile Guardian feature. Campus shuttle buses are tracked via GPS signals. Students love the fact that they can monitor the bus location and keep studying (or developing important lifetime social skills) to the very last minute before rushing out to catch the bus.

Students and parents both love that a student can set a tracking timer for anywhere from a few minutes to a few hours through the Mobile Guardian. The system tracks their location and if they don't deactivate the tracker before the timer expires, the campus police will call them to make sure they are okay and will know their precise location if there's any problem.

"It is important for students to know that they are safe and comfortable in their environment, but I would say it is even more important for the parents," remarks Dr. Pennington. "The Mobile Guardian feature allows a student to send an alert in a passive mode to the police station that they have activated Guardian and they want to be tracked. They want people to know where they are."

Campus safety is one of the top criteria parents use in evaluating a university. Academic capabilities and social opportunities certainly also play a critical role as students choose where they want to spend four years preparing for the rest of their lives.

To ensure overall success, the program had to first gain the acceptance and adoption of students. That required intense focus on community and safety features that appeal much more strongly to students than the rest of the university community.

"This is a journey. At the outset we were very concerned with providing a network with the quality of service and capacity to support our rapidly expanding population of users. In hindsight, I wish we'd invested more time getting key faculty and support team members fully on board from the beginning of the journey," Dr. Chapel notes. "These mobile devices have the potential to be powerful tools in the learning environment. We have created a plateau from which we intend to greatly expand the use of this

CASE STUDY (CONTINUED)

technology as an integral part of the campus curriculum. We have very creative professors who I'm confident will find new ways to unleash the power of mobility in preparing our students for the future.''

By building mobility into all critical aspects of what they offer, Montclair State University has differentiated itself from other universities and started to redefine how higher education operates.

''It is a good feeling to know that your university is paving the way for something that I think will ultimately become part of the culture of higher education across the country,'' concludes Dr. Cole.

Have you heard of Montclair State University? Many haven't, but they will. The school's innovative approaches to creating a richer, safer, and more connected campus experience have contributed to their position as New Jersey's fastest growing university.

Note

1. "U.S. Education Vertical Telecom Services Markets," Frost & Sullivan, 2006.

CHAPTER 11

Protect
Manage the Danger
of Moblity

T he previous chapters describe how businesses can capture the power of mobility to create tremendous differentiation as mobility gets built into every product, service, and process. As noted there, capturing the power of mobility will be full of challenges. In some respects, these challenges can be viewed as dangers of mobility to be managed.

However, this chapter deals with more mundane dangers that all companies will face as mobility becomes integrated into how we do business. Whether or not a company chooses to capture the power of the new technology, it will need to manage the danger. Even businesses that fail to use mobility to lead their industries in creating differentiation eventually will need to adopt mobility to close the gap created by their competitors.

What Are These Dangers?

An entire book could be written on the dangers that we can already see from mobility. Unfortunately, new dangers will emerge as mobility is increasingly integrated into how we live and work, so this chapter should not be viewed as a comprehensive checklist against which you should manage your mobility risk. However, history also gives us a solid foundation for understanding the general areas of challenge that businesses will face.

In short, we should be prepared to manage three key interrelated classes of danger:

1. Data security

2. Financial exposure

3. Third-party claims

Data Security

Perhaps the greatest danger related to mobility is that mobile devices are, well, mobile. They go everywhere. And sometimes they don't come back. Mobile devices, including cell phones, smart phones, and laptop computers are attractive targets for thieves because they are, by design, easy to carry away. But these devices are also small enough that they can easily slip out of a pocket, purse, or briefcase without being noticed. And honestly, we're human and sometimes we just forget to pick them up after we've set them down.

According to a research report from Pointsec Mobile Technologies, 8,701 electronic devices were left in taxicabs in the Washington, D.C.–Baltimore area during a six-month period in 2006. Over 6,000 of these devices were mobile phones. Eighty percent were eventually reunited with their owners. Another 339 laptops were left in cabs in the Washington–Baltimore area, all of which found their way home.[1]

London travelers apparently are less diligent in tracking down their lost devices. According to another Pointsec study, around five laptops and ten mobile phones are handed in at Heathrow Airport each day, most of which were simply forgotten at security checkpoints. Only 60% of these devices are reclaimed by their owners. After three months, the devices are sold at auction. By Pointsec's math, that translates into 730 laptops and 1,460 mobile phones auctioned off each year. Imagine the wealth of sensitive competitive information being auctioned off by Heathrow each year![2]

The danger to companies from these lost and stolen devices is twofold. On one hand, many mobile devices store important company information that could damage your business or help a competitor. Mark Komisky, chief executive of Bluefire Security Technologies Inc., was quoted by the *Washington Post* describing his panic when he lost his smart phone. The device stored e-mails, details of his company's strategy, and phone numbers of executives at Bluefire's most strategic partners. Thankfully, as a security company, Bluefire had put in place the mechanisms to remotely erase the information from the device.[3]

Wired magazine reported on a BlackBerry that had been owned by a Morgan Stanley vice president of mergers and acquisitions that was sold on eBay. The buyer had full access to the address book of Morgan Stanley executives and clients, debt-restructuring strategies for specific companies, e-mails on preliminary talks for potential merger deals, financial spreadsheets, and other documents that, at the very least, could inform a competitor's understanding of how Morgan Stanley conducts its business.[4]

The second threat from these lost or stolen devices is the configuration information that the device owner uses to connect securely into corporate networks. Even if the new owner of the device can't access any sensitive information stored on the device, they may be able to access your networks and find a way to access confidential information stored elsewhere in your business.

When dealing with mobile network users, the process should follow the policies that have developed over the years for any user connecting into the network. The first step is authentication—are you who you say you are? The second step is interrogation to determine whether the connecting device represents any type of threat—are the security policy requirements met and is the device free of viruses and other malware. Based on that information, a decision can be made as to whether any issues can be remedied and what level of access will be allowed.

Another major area of threat to data security comes from criminals tapping into your networks without using a lost or stolen device. Network hacking is not a new profession, so many of the tools developed over the years to defend against attacks, detect them when they occur, and to limit the exposure from an attack are just as valuable for wireless networks. However, wireless networks also represent new forms of threat. Wireless messages passing through the air to and from your employees' devices can theoretically be intercepted, and even the data flowing across wired networks from mobile employees are at risk, for example when connecting through a public WiFi access point or when connecting through a hotel's network. Employees need to be kept informed as network hackers move beyond today's tricks, like WiFi spoofing, into new areas of deception.

Use of a mobile virtual private network (VPN), including encryption of data to the device can go a long way toward securing your sensitive information that is flying through the air.

Mobility also introduces new data security threats through the proliferation of camera phones into the workplace. In all businesses, across all technology eras, the greatest security threats have come from those we trust—employees and partners—those who walk through our doors each day and have access to sensitive information. Camera phones represent a new tool for trusted criminals to walk out the door with our secrets. Maintaining control and visibility over the mobile devices in use by employees is a good first step toward minimizing this threat.

Financial Exposure

Of course, any of the risks associated with data security threats can easily translate into financial exposure, but mobility also introduces new forms of expense into the business.

The most obvious new expenses are from mobile devices and the service plans to keep your employees connected. U.S. wireless carriers currently heavily subsidize most mobile devices in exchange for long-term commitments to use a given carrier's service, but even if you negotiate for a heavy subsidy, smart phones that are best positioned to deliver the power of mobility for your employees likely will cost several hundred dollars apiece. It's also not unusual for monthly voice and data service fees per employee to be in the $50 to $100 range or perhaps even higher for your most mobile communications–intensive workers.

You may think that you've got it easy if employees are already using their personal mobile devices to do their work. It might appear that you're getting the benefits of mobility without having to pay for them. However, I'm guessing that at least some of those employees are expensing back their mobility costs to the company. These somewhat invisible costs are even more dangerous since they are unmanaged and can't benefit from the negotiating power of your entire firm. Even worse, the devices and connections likely are also unmanaged, opening the company up to mostly invisible security risks. Carefully consider the costs and benefits of each approach before assuming that the status quo is financially attractive.

In addition to the basic mobile communications device, you likely will also consider enabling your workforce with applications that are specifically suited to increasing their productivity in their jobs. Depending on the application, purchasing and deploying these applications will likely incur up-front costs and may also have ongoing recurring charges. Undoubtedly, in deploying these applications, you will have evaluated the business case and have justified the additional expense, but these costs do represent new incremental items that likely haven't previously been in your budget.

Finally, be sure to plan for your own internal staff needs to support a newly mobilized workforce. What you have traditionally called *desktop support* and *network support* will now take on entirely new responsibilities that likely will require additional headcount and cross-training in new technologies and applications.

And keep in mind that mobile technology is advancing rapidly, so you should plan for a shorter refresh cycle than you currently enjoy with PCs and other assets. You may be able to squeeze two years of use for handsets for most of your employees, but power users may need to be upgraded every year.

To get a sense for the impact of these types of technology changes, J. Gold Associates analyzed the costs associated with switching from one mobile e-mail system to another. Their analysis concluded that the cost of switching was $845 per user, with the cost split evenly between information technology (IT) infrastructure and end-user deployment costs.[5]

Beyond your IT budget, mobilizing your workforce also introduces financial risk in the form of lost productivity. Workers who previously relied on paper-driven processes may have been less efficient, but their pens and pads worked everywhere, all the time. Unfortunately, the same cannot be said for mobile technology. Device and network failures can cause your team members to be stuck, sitting idle waiting for a replacement or the network to recover instead of being able to do their jobs.

Other threats to employee productivity include the temptation to play games or surf the mobile Internet (remember the early days of Windows as workers discovered Solitaire and when the Mosaic browser opened new worlds for employees to explore), and interruptions that come now that your employees can be reached anytime, anywhere for both business and personal needs. Obviously, this is more of a management challenge than a technology challenge, and these issues will be more of a problem for some employees than others, but don't overlook the need to actively incorporate these new challenges into your management team's supervisory and coaching activities.

Finally, mobile devices are increasingly becoming targets for malware—software intended to do damage. Mobile viruses, worms, Trojan horse programs, and spyware are beginning to show up on mobile devices. These pests invade using the same tricks that PC crackers have used in the Internet era—getting installed with "free" software, riding along with e-mail attachments, and sneaking in through infected Web pages. But mobility represents a new threat as well, with some viruses spreading through the Bluetooth connections most typically turned on for cordless headsets. All of the major vendors of PC-based antivirus software are introducing mobile products to help ward off attacks.

And these attacks can be expensive. In addition to lost productivity for the handset owner, IT resources are often consumed cleaning up the mess. Critical data may be lost. And some attacks result in a significant increase in network traffic, resulting in financial exposure for network fees.

Third-Party Claims

The final area of danger closely follows from the risks to data security and financial exposure. Mobility can open your firm to new forms of third-party claims against your company and new flavors of old third-party claims.

Following directly from the threat of data loss when a mobile device is lost or stolen is the liability that comes from your firm's failure to properly protect that data. The list of companies and government entities that have been exposed to the possibility of significant third-party claims continues to grow. Just as a sample, here's a list of events from May and June 2006:

- U.S. Department of Veterans Affairs lost a laptop containing personal information on 26.5 million veterans and active-duty soldiers.
- New York state government lost a laptop with 540,000 names.
- Ernst & Young Global Ltd. lost a laptop with 243,000 names.

- YMCA of Greater Providence, Rhode Island, lost a laptop with 68,000 names.
- ING Groep NV lost a laptop with 13,000 names.
- Equifax Inc. lost a laptop with 291 names.

In each of these cases, data was lost that could contribute to the growing problem of identity theft. Because of these potential liabilities, the costs associated with a lost device are significantly higher than just the price of a replacement. At least 35 states have passed laws placing additional burdens on companies that have a security breach that involves personal information.

Every year, the Computer Security Institute with participation from the San Francisco Federal Bureau of Investigation's Computer Intrusion Squad conducts a survey of computer security practitioners in U.S. corporations, government agencies, financial and medical institutions, and universities. The 2006 survey included 616 responses. While the percentage of respondents reporting laptop or mobile theft held relatively flat at 47%, the losses increased by more than half from $19,562 per respondent to $30,057 from 2005 to 2006.[6]

Such data security failures can also trigger regulatory violations including the Health Insurance Portability and Accountability Act (HIPAA), Gramm-Leach-Bliley, and Sarbanes-Oxley. For example, HIPAA clearly states that patient data must be protected against unauthorized disclosure with penalties for failure to adequately protect that data.

But even new forms of third-party claims are emerging, and these are coming from the very employees that are being empowered with mobile technology. The fact that mobile technology enables us to work anywhere, anytime has led to us working everywhere and all the time. This creates a variety of potential dangers.

A recent article in Britain's *The Independent* reported on three such dangers that have translated into employee lawsuits. In one, a business consultant is suing her employer for damages because she was constantly checking her BlackBerry for messages, which led to her marriage collapsing and her losing custody of her children. In a second case cited by the paper, a woman sued her employer because she was so distracted by her BlackBerry that she put cleaning fluid on her baby's diaper instead of baby oil. And in a third case, a company ended up paying substantial damages to an employee who was using her BlackBerry while driving, resulting in a crash that killed a motorcyclist.[7]

Obviously, in each of these tragic cases, the primary fault is with the employee, but as we push mobile technology onto our employees and raise our expectations of their availability, responsiveness, and performance, lawsuits such as these are sure to follow. Teaching managers to restrain their expectations is an important step, but official policies that employees may sign up to as they are empowered with mobile technology can also be an important tool in managing your firm's liability.

Policies can also play an important role in keeping employees happy in the workplace. As cell phones have become increasingly media capable, new risks and challenges have emerged. Perhaps the most openly discussed is the challenge of personally selected ringtones. According to a workplace survey by staffing company Randstad USA, 30% of employees listed cell phones ringing as one of their top workplace pet peeves.[8] Some companies have established policies requiring cell phones to be set to vibrate in the workplace to combat this contributor to worker stress.

However, the topic that may be even more dangerous to companies deals with pornography and other content that can create a hostile environment for employees. Employees every day are carrying into the workplace personal devices with multimedia capabilities that exceed what many of them go home to in their private homes every night. This opportunity to take personal content wherever they go can create new challenges for employers as we strive to maintain a healthy and productive workplace.

Taming the Dangers

Two critical steps are required to keep the potential dangers of mobility from bankrupting your company.

The first is to update your company policies to reflect the new realities of the mobility age. Employees need clear guidance on what they can and can't do to keep your business out of trouble. Policies should address the dangers represented in this chapter:

- Protecting company assets and data.
- Ensuring secure mobile access to company networks.
- Minimizing expenses related to devices, service plans, applications, and associated infrastructure.
- Effectively receiving support needed to maintain productivity.
- Minimizing personal and nonproductive use of mobile devices during work hours.
- Restricting the use of mobile devices while driving.

- Appropriately limiting expectations for work-related activities beyond normal work hours.

- Reducing ringtone-induced workplace stress.

- Controlling mobile content in the work environment.

Of course, policies are useless if no one knows about them. Ensure that every employee agrees to your mobility policies when they are issued and that every new employee agrees to them as they join the company.

The second critical step is to ensure that you have established an effective support infrastructure so that you are getting the full benefit of your investment in mobilizing your business. This includes establishing a knowledgeable support staff that is able to respond to workers who are trying to be productive anywhere, anytime. It includes putting in place the hardware and software infrastructure required to manage the security and reliability of your mobile assets. It includes a commitment to ongoing monitoring of new technology advances and the willingness to refresh your infrastructure as mobility continues to advance.

This is a big commitment. Especially in these early days of mobility, it's probably worth considering outsourcing to experts for at least part of the deployment or ongoing support.

In any case, managing all of the dangers of mobility may sound expensive, and in reality may represent significant new expenditures. These costs should be factored into your overall evaluation of the value of mobilizing your products, services, and processes. When balanced against the value created by mobility, these costs may not seem so expensive.

FROM THE REAL WORLD

Sprint's Mobility Management Services

The following content is provided by Sprint Nextel, Inc.

Sprint Mobility Management is an award-winning suite of managed services that allows your company to securely manage the wireless devices, data, rate plans, and user profiles throughout your enterprise. The suite is comprised of three primary sets of options: Billing Management, Device Management, and Security Management.

BILLING MANAGEMENT

A billing analytics service that provides a robust, easy-to-use Web portal to manage mobile communications. Billing Management enables businesses to:

- Control wireless spending:
  - ○ Consolidated view of accounts and expenses.
  - ○ Visibility of corporate wireless plan by user profile and department, including trending, usage and overage expenses.
  - ○ Enforce and monitor expense policies.

DEVICE MANAGEMENT

Device Management offers businesses the ability to manage multi-carrier mobile devices via a self-service Web portal. Device Management enables business to:

- Manage devices from multiple carriers:
  - ○ Manage multiple user configurations and profiles.
  - ○ Synchronize data, files, and applications.

- ○ Deploy software updates.

- ○ View software and hardware inventory.

- ○ Backup and restore files and applications.

- ○ Push all functions Over the Air (OTA).

Security Management

Sprint Mobile Security provides end-to-end security for laptops and handheld devices. Mobile Security enables businesses to:

- Enforce corporate compliance:

  - ○ Manage devices, data, and security policies from a single Web portal.

  - ○ Update noncompliant programs with automatic remediation.

- Secure corporate data:

  - ○ Flexible security with device "kill" or "lock."

  - ○ Enforce password policies across all devices.

  - ○ Encrypt data on mobile devices and memory cards.

  - ○ Allow users to securely connect to the corporate intranet.

- Prevent internal and external threats:

  - ○ Monitor and control network access.

  - ○ Detect and automatically protect against viruses, worms, and malicious code.

Customer Care

At Sprint, we provide multiple levels of support allowing you to define exactly how much control you have over your mobile environment. Customer Care includes:

- Multicarrier support for multiple devices.

- Premium level of support available 24/7.

- 24-hour fulfillment for Sprint phones.

FROM THE REAL WORLD (CONTINUED)

- Self-care Web portal.
- Reporting and activity logs.

Case Study

AllState GES

AllState GES, an appliance distribution and installation company in the Phoenix area, is focused on delivering good products at a great price when the customer needs them.

That mission requires a three-way focus on quality, cost, and time management that can be hard to balance. To help make those goals become a reality, AllState turned to Xora, a mobility software company. By installing Xora's TimeTrack software on their employees' cell phones, AllState can track the location and project-specific activities of their team members.

When it comes to a quality installation, proper site preparation is critical. AllState clearly communicates to its customers the required condition of the site for a successful project. When AllState installers arrive on-site, they type into their phone the job number, clocking into the project. They also key in any conditions on the job site such as existing damage or any issues with site readiness. Using the camera built into their phone, they can also attach photos further documenting issues. These records not only are helpful in quickly resolving disputes with contractors, but in educating their customers in what is required for a successful job that lives up to AllState's quality standards.

As the AllState installers leave a job site, they clock out of the project, creating very accurate records of the time required for each

CASE STUDY (CONTINUED)

project. These records help the company to improve performance of the work force, reducing overall costs. But an even greater cost savings has been realized in the communications between the mobile workers and the AllState office. Prior to deploying the Xora software, drivers and installers would regularly call in to report their location and job status. Since automating with Xora, the number of calls to the office have been cut to less than half, saving an hour or two of telephone time each day.

"The time savings have been tremendous, but the biggest benefit to Xora is in customer service," said AllState dispatcher Jackie McCarter. "Prior to Xora we could tell customers their appliances would be delivered that day; now we can say in a two to three hour window."

That precision comes from the real-time information the office has on the mobile workers' location and job status. Jackie and her teammates can see where each installation team is at any time on a Web-based map, and can view the comments being typed by field workers through a Web-based reporting tool, enabling the company to not only deliver appliances when their customers need them, but to predict that delivery time with great precision.

Quality service, when you need it, at a competitive cost. Isn't that what all of us want from our suppliers? By mobilizing their workforce, AllState has managed to step up their performance on all three competitive dimensions. Their customers have got to love that!

Notes

1. Pointsec press release. 2006. "New Survey Reveals Thousands of Mobile Devices Left Behind in Major U.S. City Taxi Cabs,"

November 28, www.pointsec.com/news/newsreleases/release
.cfm?PressId=386.

2. Pointsec press release. 2006. "40% of Mobiles Left at Airports This
Summer Will Never Be Reclaimed," August 31, www.pointsec
.com/news/newsreleases/release.cfm?PressId=313.

3. "Lost a Blackberry? Data Could Open a Security Breach."
Washington Post, July 25, 2005, p. A01.

4. Zetter, Kim. 2003. "BlackBerry Reveals Bank's Secrets." *Wired
News,* August 25, www.wired.com/news/business/1,600520
.html.

5. J. Gold Associates press release. 2006. "J. Gold Associates Releases
Report on the High Cost of Change in Wireless E-mail," January
13, www.jgoldassociates.com.

6. CSI/FBI Computer Crime and Security Survey, 2006.

7. Goodchild, Sophie, and Martin Hodgson. 2006. "CrackBerry
Addicts: Why the Workers Who Can't Switch Off Are Suing
Their Employers," *The Independent,* October 1, http://news
.independent.co.uk/world/science_technology/article1777821.ece.

8. Randstad USA press release. 2006. "Loud Talkers among Biggest
Workplace Pet Peeves, According to Randstad Survey," March 14,
http://us.randstad.com/webapp/internet/servlet/News?id=53.

CHAPTER 12

Learn from Your Customers

I f you've taken the steps described so far in this book, you're on a great path toward capturing the power of mobility, and you're already creating new value for your customers and translating that power into value for your employees and owners. That's great!

But, almost definitely, you still haven't captured the full power of mobility for your customers. In reality, you simply can't know how your customers and employees are going to change their behaviors once you take the first steps into mobility.

But that's not a bad thing.

It's critical to take the first steps. But it's at least as critical that you do not stop there, but rather that you learn from your customers how to make your mobilized product, service, or process even more powerful!

Sounds easy enough.

But, unfortunately, listening to customers is a skill that does not come naturally to most of us. Really listening and really learning from your customers will require intense focus and likely will require significant changes in your business.

Can you remember the last time you made a specific change in your business because of a specific comment from a specific customer? Sure, most of us do customer surveys and we use those generalized results to guide decisions we make about products and pricing and perhaps how we interact with our customers. But, as we'll discuss, survey percentages do not really teach us the innovative ways that our customers are taking our products to the next level.

Can you remember the last time you made a specific recommendation to a company you do business with and actually saw the resulting change? I can't. In fact, most of us rarely bother providing constructive input because we come to accept the fact that it never does any good.

Can we break that cycle?

It's hard on both sides, but I would argue that it is well worth it. It's hard for us to change our companies to be good at listening to customers and acting on their recommendations. And it's hard to get our customers to actually start giving us input with the confidence that it will make a difference.

So, how can you make the change?

I suggest that learning from your customers requires that you achieve three imperatives and that you pursue those imperatives through three progressive levels of learning from your customers.

The Three Imperatives

The three imperatives are:

1. Make it easy.

194

2. Make it count.

3. Pay it back.

Make It Easy

If we want to learn from our customers, we need to be willing to go to them. We need to respect what they can teach us and eliminate all barriers to their fully sharing with us what we need to learn. In the different levels of learning, this will take on different meanings, as we will see through the rest of this chapter.

Make It Count

The reason most of us never provide input to companies is that we doubt it will really make a difference. If we truly want to learn from our customers, and if we want to change the attitude of those customers toward helping us learn, then we need to do something meaningful with what they tell us. We need to make their input count. If they recommend changes to our product or service, we need to seriously consider those changes. It's as simple as that.

Pay It Back

Customer insights are valuable. We need to reward our customers for sharing them with us. Again, this takes different shapes for the different levels of learning, but we need to "pay" for the value they are creating—perhaps in the form of acknowledging their input or perhaps in more tangible forms, such as discounts and free add-ons.

The Levels of Learning

The three levels of learning are:

1. Listen
2. Engage
3. Employ

Listen

How easy do you make it for customers to give you unsolicited input on how your product or service could be improved? Do you force them to conform to your way of interacting, or will you "come to their house" and accept their feedback on their terms?

If they are most comfortable doing business through the Internet, how easy is it to provide feedback through your Web site? If there's a friendly form, is it easy to find? Is it easy for them to find an e-mail address that clearly communicates that at that address you welcome product or service ideas and feedback?

How easy is it to find a phone number where customers can call you? When they call, how frustrating is their experience? Is one of their first options the opportunity to provide you with product or service input? Is there an option to actually talk to a knowledgeable person about your products or services? Do you limit the hours when calls are accepted to hours that may be inconvenient for your customer?

Your answers to these questions may indicate that you are loudly telling your customers that you have no interest in learning from them. You do not want to hear what they have to say. Or your answers may indicate that you are listening with open ears and an open mind.

Even if you have made it easy for your customers to tell you what they think, do you make their input count? Who sees or hears what your customers tell you? Do you ever make changes based on input from your customers?

In a recent Harvard Business School *Working Knowledge* article, HBS professor Frances X. Frei identified Intuit, the financial software company, as an example of a company that makes their customers' input count. At Intuit, the customer service department resides within product development and the people fielding customer service calls take the input they receive directly to the software engineers developing the next generation of Intuit software. Intuit pays higher wages for their customer service staff to attract a different type of individual and to recognize that they are expected to do more than just open trouble tickets. The end result is higher product satisfaction and fewer but more valuable calls from customers.[1]

As another example, Mark Federman of the University of Toronto, in a speech to the Conference Board of Canada, cited a drug store chain that provided immediate responsiveness to the feedback from customers. "For instance, one of the callers to one store noted that the aspirin was on too high a shelf for her—she was short, and her arthritis prevented her from reaching up. The very next day, the aspirin was relocated to a lower shelf. That's value."[2]

It does you no good to pretend to listen to your customers but then do nothing with what they tell you, or simply bury their input into a generalized statistical result that gets broadly shared every few months.

Your product or service will not reach its full potential and your customer's cynicism will increase.

So, how do you pay customers for simply telling you what they want? For starters, truly listen. Unfortunately, in today's marketplace, so few companies are willing to listen that for customers that really care and are willing to share, finding a company willing to listen and take customers seriously is reward enough. But then, follow-through on what they say and keep them informed of progress. At the end of the day, your final update to the customer may say, "Thank you for your input. Your ideas will undoubtedly shape our future offers as we continue in our mission to deliver the best products and services in the industry. However, we have completed evaluation of your specific product idea and we are unable to justify the investment in this particular capability at this time. Please continue to share your challenges and your dreams with us. We value your partnership and your business."

Even though that message may indicate a disappointing specific outcome, more importantly it communicates that you truly value your customer's input and that you took their input seriously. Unfortunately, there are few companies that will similarly interact with their customers.

Engage

But listening is just the first step. Actively engaging with customers in an ongoing dialog creates an even richer environment for you to learn from them.

Sprint Nextel recently launched a Web site called Buzz About Wireless (www.buzzaboutwireless.com) intended to provide a comfortable place for customers to share their experiences, good and bad, and engage with other customers and with the company. The site provides forums where folks can talk about what they love and hate about Sprint's products and services, where they can ask questions and expect a more useful and meaningful answer than official documentation, and where they can express their desires for how they wish the company and its products to develop.

Tristan Kime, the Sprint customer experience and community manager who managed the launch of the site, acknowledges that it can be risky offering to engage with customers in a new way. "If we aren't responsive in the way that folks in online forums expect, then we can do more damage than good."

This difference was amplified in the first few days after the site launched. A customer asked in the public forums a question about the company's network plans in his state. A well-meaning Sprint employee responded with the standard company answer. Immediately, other community participants slammed the company for providing a "boilerplate" response and not truly engaging the customer's need.

Tristan and his team immediately corrected the mistake and reminded everyone helping out that engaging with customers in this way is more than just business as usual.

"We're hearing lots of good ideas from customers. One of the challenges is that evaluating the merits of each idea within our business takes time, so we have to manage customers' expectations and keep the dialog and information flowing," Tristan notes.

The Sprint team found that launching the site wasn't that hard or expensive, compared to the value of the input, feedback, and engagement. To make the launch as quick and successful as possible, the team evaluated a variety of outsource partners, selecting Lithium Technologies as the one that best fit Sprint's specific needs. The whole launch process from initial concept through live customers took less than three months.

Few companies can manage to establish a rich and engaging relationship with all of their customers. Netflix is one of those companies. When you talk to folks at Netflix, the first thing you notice is that they don't use the term *customers;* instead, they say *members.* It's easy to brush this off as corporate-speak pushed down from marketing, but the more you understand their business, the more overly formal even the term *members* seems. The conversation turns to the nature of the relationship between customer and Netflix as being more of a trusted friendship.

According to the company, more than 90% of Netflix members would recommend the company to friends,[3] and according to research firm Foresee Results, Netflix has the highest online customer satisfaction of any company in the world.[4]

How has the company established this kind of trusted relationship with customers? Although Netflix is in the business of renting DVDs, the core of the business is the company's customer software. That software keeps track of the movies and TV shows each customer has rented and the DVDs the customer has queued up to rent next. When a customer returns a movie, they are sent an e-mail reminding them to rate the movie they just watched. Most importantly, Netflix makes it simple to rate movies within the flow of a member's normal interactions, and the payback is immediate, with instantly improved recommendations. Netflix has collected more than 1.6 billion individual ratings in their database. This simple exchange allows each member to be presented with a custom view into Netflix, connecting members to the movies they will love.

The result is threefold. First, customers get all the benefits of an incredibly broad portfolio of titles (more than 70,000 and growing) without the pain of needing to wade through thousands of uninteresting titles to find the one they might enjoy. Second, the value to the customer increases with every rental and every review (the more movies I review, the better targeted are the recommendations to me). Third, the customer sees value in providing input to Netflix. In short, Netflix has nailed the "Make it easy," "Make it count," and "Pay it back" imperatives I mentioned earlier.

But the company does not stop at customer ratings and great recommendations. Netflix overinvests in customer research. While the methodologies are not significantly different from the surveys, focus groups, and experiential research that other firms perform, the existing trusted dialog with the customer and the company's customer database seem to enable Netflix to get feedback faster and with greater richness than most companies.

An example of how the company has used that feedback is the Previews feature through the Netflix Web site. Customers said they would love to easily watch the kind of preview trailers that typically precede a movie in the theater. Netflix was able to leverage its software to dramatically improve on that process. Now, when a member opens the preview feature, they see a continuous stream of preview trailers that are specifically selected and sequenced based on what the customer will love, and it is simple to order a movie directly from the Previews section.[5]

Unfortunately, not all companies have the luxury of the software and database capabilities on which Netflix has built its business. How can the rest of us hope to engage in a meaningful dialog with our customers?

A recent article by Jennifer Alsever at BNET.com provides some valuable direction. In the article, titled "How to Get Your Customers to Solve Problems for You," Jennifer recommends four key steps to "harness the intelligence of customers that love your business":

1. Decide if you really care what customers think.
   o Engage in a true dialog with your customers, or don't bother at all.

2. Learn who loves you (and who hates you).
   o Identify customers who will provide the most useful insight.

3. Make engaged customers feel special.
   o Reward passionate consumers with insider perks and benefits.

4. Bring customers inside the tent.
   o Give participants clear goals and integrate their ideas into your decision making.

As Jennifer notes, one of the critical steps is to find the right customers to engage with. She recommends looking for the customers that contact you the most often—whether with positive or negative interactions. She also recommends looking for the most active participants in online forums that discuss your firm's products or services. These are the folks that have demonstrated that they care and that they want to be heard. When you reach out to them, they will engage and they will value the dialog—if you make it count and are willing to make changes based on their input.[6]

So, now that you've opened a dialog with customers so you can learn from them how to improve your product, what do you ask?

BDC Consulting, a service of the Business Development Bank of Canada (BDC), recommends a discussion flow that asks three key questions:

1. What are the top three problems your product or service should solve?

2. What are three things they dislike about your product or service?

3. What are the top three things they would add to your product or service?[7]

These questions are likely to lead to a rich discussion that will help you better understand the strengths of your product and the opportunities to create new value for your customers.

Employ

The final level of learning from your customers is to actually put them to work!

My favorite example of a company that does this well is the Lego Group. The company offers free Lego Digital Designer software that makes it easy for customers to design their own custom building sets. Those designs are then uploaded to legofactory.com, where they can be ordered. The custom sets then arrive in the mail in a box with a picture of the customer's unique design on the front. Customers can even make their designs available for others to purchase.

The Lego Group doesn't just passively observe this customer activity. The company has taken several sets designed by customers and fully productized them—giving them traditional Lego packaging (with the addition of the designers' photos) and making them available in Lego stores, catalogs, and the company's main online store. The designers even get paid royalties![8]

However, even the designs that don't turn into official products inform Lego's ongoing product development. Those that visit legofactory.com are the most passionate customers, and the time they invest in designing a new creation represents what they really wish Lego was selling!

But Lego doesn't stop there. When the company was beginning work on a new version of its Mindstorms robotic building set, they identified a handful of the most passionate and talented Mindstorms customers from around the world. This "Mindstorms User Panel" (MUP) actively worked with the company over 11 months leading up to the formal introduction of the Mindstorms NXT. The MUP members were invited to Lego headquarters in Denmark and played a critical role in helping the company introduce a product that was a hit right out of the gate. What did it cost Lego? Well, they paid their MUP "employees" in Legos and with the honor of making their input count.[9]

However far you are willing to go, your customers are ready to go with you. Take the time to learn from them, and together you can capture more power from mobility than you ever could have imagined on your own!

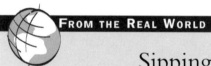

FROM THE REAL WORLD

Sipping Their
Own Champagne

TechSmith (www.techsmith.com) is the world's leading provider of screen capture and recording software. The company's flagship product, SnagIt, is recognized worldwide as the premier tool for capturing an image of the computer screen for use in documents, presentations, and for training purposes. The company has extended that leadership into a number of related areas

Two of TechSmith's products particularly relevant to learning from your customers are UserVue and Morae.

UserVue™ is a Web-based service that allows a product manager to remotely connect to, interact with, observe and record users as they navigate an application or Web site. UserVue shares the participant's screen, providing a truly accurate view of the user experience. Up to ten people can view a live session and collaborate over chat, without disturbing the participant. As soon as a session ends, the product manager can create a Windows Media Video (WMV) file of the recording to view and share. You can analyze, edit, and share UserVue recordings in Morae Manager.[10]

Morae is a complete, all-digital application for user experience research. It enables organizations to observe and record how customers really interact with a Web site or application. By showing a product manager not just *what* actions the user took, but also *why* and *how,* Morae gives them a complete and accurate understanding of user needs. Morae has three components—Recorder, Remote Viewer, and Manager. These three components work together to record, log, observe, analyze, and share the user experience.[11]

Morae Recorder captures the total user experience by recording screen video, user audio and video, and a chronicle of system events, all automatically synchronized. It also sends the screen video, camera video, and audio to observers using Remote Viewer. Anyone logged into a Remote Viewer can observe the recording session and set markers, with text notes, to flag important moments. This marker information can be searched for and viewed later using Morae Manager. Within Morae Manager, you can import recordings and quickly analyze the data and calculate metrics. The integrated editing functionality makes it easy to assemble the important moments into a highlight video to share.[12]

What better way to learn from your customers than to actually watch how they use your product—the challenges they encounter, the rabbit trails they pursue, and the frustration they display on their faces and express under their breath.

Obviously, TechSmith believes in the value of learning from customers! And, of course, the company uses its own products to watch how people use TechSmith products and the TechSmith Web site to accomplish specific tasks. For example, in preparing for the 8.0 release of SnagIt, the company brought in a variety of users and used Morae to observe the usability challenges with the current release of the product.

The resulting SnagIt 8 benefited tremendously from what customers were able to teach the company, making the product approachable to a new, much broader set of customers. "With SnagIt 8, we are knocking down barriers and bringing screen capture to new audiences," said Tony Dunckel, product manager at TechSmith. "We've brought the most popular features to the forefront so new users can realize immediate benefits while still having the option to customize SnagIt for maximum effectiveness. The learning curve has essentially been eliminated. New users can be up and running within minutes after installing SnagIt 8, and we've enhanced SnagIt's editing capabilities, including PDF output, so users don't have to use additional and expensive software to embellish their captures."[13]

But TechSmith doesn't stop there. Formal usability testing and watching your customers use your products are great ways to learn how to improve, but the company also creates opportunities for customers to talk and listens carefully to what they have to say.

Betsy Weber, chief evangelist for TechSmith, estimates that she attends 30 trade shows a year. Even though her title implies that her job is to talk, Betsy acknowledges that it's much more valuable to listen.

At a trade show, it's not unusual for customer to show up and share their perspectives on what they like and don't like about TechSmith products. Betsy is not shy about grabbing a Webcam and having the customer speak through it, creating an internal video document, complete with nonverbal nuances, that then gets shared with the product development teams back in Michigan.

Betsy has also led creation of a number of customer advisory boards, organized by product line and by industry vertical focus. TechSmith has established online group discussion areas where these customers can talk to each other and share their questions and perspectives about TechSmith products. Throughout the development process, the company will introduce these customers to ideas and demos being considered for future releases and collect feedback on initial reactions, what the board members like, and what they don't like.

"It's critical that we recruit a very diverse set of members for our boards. We make sure that we have people who love our products and folks who may be our biggest critics," Betsy notes. "We also look for diversity, from newbies to power users, to make sure that we're neither turning our back on our base nor missing out on opportunities to reach new customers."

So, how does Betsy find these advisory board members? She looks for them everywhere she goes, and she has help. She asks people that approach her at industry events who have passion for TechSmith products (positive or negative) if they'd like to help make TechSmith products better. She e-mails folks who are passionate in blogs and technical forums. The company's technical support team knows that Betsy wants to hear about the folks who are trying to use their products in new and unusual ways.

And recruit them she does. All she has to offer is the opportunity to be heard and the chance to really make a difference in improving

TechSmith's products. So far, TechSmith has recruited over 600 participants to its advisory boards and beta test groups.

Obviously, TechSmith is one company that not only sells the tools to learn from your customers, but lives that opportunity itself.

When I asked Betsy if the readers of this book could expect Tech-Smith to come out with mobility-focused tools so we can all learn from our customers, characteristically, her response was, "That's an interesting idea. I'll take it back to the development team."

Thanks Betsy. I couldn't ask for a better answer.

Case Study

Portable On Demand Storage

Portable On Demand Storage (PODS®) is revolutionizing the moving and storage industry through the power of mobility!

Storage has always been fixed. You go to a storage location and you put your stuff into the storage container or building. When you want your stuff again, you go back to where you stored it and you get it out.

That sounds simple enough—and we have been willing to put up with that model forever because we could not imagine any other approach. The founders of PODS were able to see well beyond the assumption that storage is always fixed.

In 1998, by taking something that had always been fixed and making it mobile, the company created tremendous new value for people needing to store or move their stuff:

- Saving customers time and money.

- Making both on-site and dry storage more convenient and accessible for the customer.

- Eliminating many of the complexities and stress associated with moving and storage.

- Putting customers in control of how they moved and stored their belongings, with as much or as little help packing as they wanted.

- Making moving and storage safer and more secure.

- Creating a totally different relationship between the customer and his or her moving/storage company—one based on superior service and trust.[14]

Today, PODS offers service to over 200 million people in more than 20,000 cities in 53 states, provinces, and territories throughout the United States, Canada, and Australia. In 2006, the company rolled out its 100,000th PODS brand storage container and served its 500,000th customer reservation.[15]

This phenomenal growth has come from taking a service that has always been assumed to be fixed and making it mobile.

PODS introduced the concept of portable storage containers that are delivered to the customer. With PODS, the customer packs the storage container at his leisure and doesn't have to worry about finding a friend with a pickup truck or making lots of trips back and forth to the storage location. When the container is fully loaded, PODS comes and picks it up again, taking it to the PODS warehouse. When the customer is ready to unpack, at the original or their new location, PODS delivers the container, and once again the customer has complete control over unloading at his convenience and with minimal effort.[16]

Of course, there's a reason that storage has always been non-mobile.

For one thing, storage buildings are designed to withstand the weather. Part of PODS's innovation has been to create a portable container that is as weather resistant as a fixed-location storage building. PODS containers come in two sizes: 8 feet by 8 feet by 12 feet and 8 feet by 8 feet by 16 feet. They are made with steel frame construction, a marine-grade wood interior, and aluminum skin exterior. They are designed to withstand winds up to 110 miles per hour.[17]

For another thing, once I pile my boxes of eight-track cartridges on top of my old dorm room sofa and lay my ten-speed bike on top of all of that, I'm not sure jerking that big box around is such a wise idea. Packing a PODS container may require a bit more care and wisdom than throwing stuff into a fixed storage building, but to minimize the challenges, PODS invented the Podzilla lift and transport system—a hydraulic system that picks up the storage container and keeps it as steady as possible during transportation to and from the warehouse.[18]

Finally, when I take my stuff to a storage building, I know exactly where it is. When the PODS truck drives off with all my stuff, how do I know where it's going?

"By definition, we are a business on the move," notes Peter S. Warhurst, president and CEO of PODS. "Keeping track of the containers holding our customers' precious belongings and our drivers could only be met with an innovative wireless solution."

PODS has implemented a solution that increases customer peace of mind. The company's 700 drivers and 200 warehouse staff use a mobile device from Motorola, wireless services and Advanced Wireless Solutions from Sprint Nextel, and software custom designed by PODS to keep a constant eye on each customer's container throughout the entire process. The solution incorporates bar code scanning, customer signature capture, and global positioning system (GPS) technologies to tie together containers to customers to precise location information. At any point in time, the company knows exactly where every container is. Since, most of the time, those containers are either at the customer's location or in the PODS limited-access warehouse, customers can feel more comfortable that their precious belongings are safe and secure than in traditional storage facilities.[19]

"We know our business and have developed the systems that create our sustainable business advantage," observes Tammy Carr, VP of corporate training and development for PODS and executive lead of the project. "But we wanted a partner who knows wireless and knew how to combine the right communications technologies to deliver a solution that meets our business needs. Sprint brought that value to our partnership."

PODS is also leveraging these technologies to be as responsive as possible to customer requests. When a customer requests their container out of the warehouse, the company can instantly locate the container and, as quickly as possible, load it onto a truck. On every trip to customer locations, drivers are guided by GPS-enabled voice navigation to ensure the most efficient route and to eliminate wasted time searching for an address. Drivers are also provided with precise customer information to ensure authorized transfer of the containers to each customer.[20]

"Our technology platform ensures that deliveries and pickups are on time," said Peter. "This provides control and visibility into the customer experience from start to finish: from quoting and booking to final delivery, resulting in a worry-free experience for the customer."

PODS introduced the wireless solution to nearly 1,000 personnel in over 150 company-owned and franchise locations. This user population had very diverse levels of technology skills, technical support staff, and buy-in to the program.

CASE STUDY (CONTINUED)

"Training was essential to meet the needs of teaching a typically computer illiterate delivery driver team on the use of the handheld device," Tammy recalls. "We met that need by using a variety of technology-based training tools such as simulation training, webinars, and our online University of PODS Virtual Classroom. Location management teams were supported by a 'T-minus-21-day' Countdown to Success Calendar of Events and CD based 'Managers Toolkit.' The Corporate Training team prepared warehouse and delivery teams before the handhelds arrived to ensure success and an expedient launch."

The wireless solution has resulted in measurable improvements in efficiency and has been well received by most employees and locations.

"We are a company not unfamiliar with using technology as a solution to improvement," concludes Tammy. "Obviously, we believe in the power of mobility and we look forward to continued improvement in our process efficiencies and asset management while pushing the wireless technology envelope wide open!"

Notes

1. Lagace, Martha. 2004. "Your Customers: Use Them or Lose Them," Harvard Business School *Working Knowledge,* July 19, http://hbswk.hbs.edu/item/4267.html.

2. "Listening to the Voice of the Customer," presented by Mark Federman, Chief Strategist, McLuhan Management Studies, McLuhan Program in Culture and Technology, Univeristy of Toronto, Luncheon Keynote, Conference Board of Canada, Customer Relationship Management Conference,

November 28, 2001. Copyright © 2001 by Mark Federman. www.utoronto. ca/mcluhan/VoiceoftheCustomer.pdf.

3. Netflix press release. 2006. "Netflix Opens Customer Service Division in Oregon and Hires Stephanie Sanford as Director," July 25, www.netflix.com/MediaCenter?id=5364.

4. Gupta, Shankar. 2006. "ForeSee: Amazon, Netflix Tops In Consumer Satisfaction," *Online Media Daily,* December 27, http://publications.mediapost.com/index.cfm?fuseaction= Articles.san&s=53040&Nid=26108&p=248134'.

5. Netflix press release. 2006. "Netflix Launches 'Previews' Feature for Instant Viewing of Movie Trailers," August 31, www .netflix.com/MediaCenter?id=5360.

6. Alsever, Jennifer. "How to Get Your Customers to Solve Problems for You, www.bnet.com/2403-13241_23-52960.html.

7. "BDC Perspective: Use Your Customers to Develop Winning Products," www.bdc.ca/en/my_project/Projects/articles/ marketing_ bdc_perspective.htm.

8. Lego press release. 2005 "Lego Group Launches Infinitely Customisable Lego Factory," November 27, http://factory.lego.com/ news/Europe%20news%20item.aspx.

9. Koerner, Brendan I. 2006. "Geeks in Toyland," *Wired News,* January 4, www.wired.com/news/culture/0,69946-0.html.

10. Mostly quoted from http://techsmith.com/uservue.asp.

11. Mostly quoted from http://techsmith.com/morae.asp.

12. Mostly quoted from http://techsmith.com/morae/features.asp.

13. TechSmith press release. 2006. "TechSmith Launches SnagIt 8; Debuts Interactive Screenshots," January 26, http://techsmith .com/company/press/pr060126.asp.

14. www.pods.com/subpages/about_pods.asp.

15. PODS press release. 2006. "PODS® Inc. Announces over 500,000 Customer Reservations and 100,000 Containers in Service—Expands National Service Market," May 17, www.pods.com/press.asp? rls_id=8.

16. www.pods.com/subpages/PODS_Innovations_Page.asp? navid=&id=8.

17. Ibid.

18. Ibid.

19. Sprint press release. 2007. "Sprint Extends Advanced Wireless Solutions to PODS to Enhance Its Delivery Capability" (draft), February.

20. Ibid.

CHAPTER 13

Conclusion: Go Capture the Power!

We started way back in Chapter 1 by recognizing that new technologies can result in dramatic impacts on society and the nature of business. We noted that a new technology can reduce the cost for a business to produce its product or it can increase the value of that product in the market. We observed that sometimes these changes are small, only incrementally improving the business, but sometimes these changes introduce radical change to business—an order of magnitude improvement—fundamentally changing the nature of the business, the nature of the product, and the reasons why customers buy the product.

By now, I hope that you have gained a vision for how mobility will impact your business. You've evaluated ways that, by building mobility into your product or service, you can increase the value of your offer to your customers. Do you think this is an incremental increase, or an order of magnitude improvement? It is important to consider how much of an impact your mobilized offer will have in the marketplace. It is also important to consider how quickly your competitors will follow you down the mobility route.

You've undoubtedly also considered ways that, by building mobility into your internal processes, you can reduce your costs or increase your revenues, resulting in increased profitability. Again, you must consider how significant an impact mobilization will have on your processes and your profitability.

Me-Too-Plus or New Category?

As you gain understanding of the magnitude of the improvement in your offer, you likely will need to consider how to position your new offer in the marketplace. In technology marketing, one of the key questions is whether your new offer represents a new category, or whether it just represents an incremental improvement to an existing category.

What's all this talk about categories?

Well, the concept of a product (or service) category is that it is a label that helps the target customer associate attributes to your product. For simplicity's sake, let's consider pizza as a familiar product category.

Everyone knows what pizza is, so when a company comes out with a new kind of pizza, customers understand the value of pizza and all they need to do is determine whether they find the incremental improvement to pizza to be appealing enough to try. For example, when Pizza Hut introduced a stuffed crust pizza, folks immediately understood the value of the offer as a pizza offer, and only had to evaluate the incremental change of the stuffed crust.

Pizza Hut didn't need to focus marketing dollars on educating their customers on a new product category. Instead, they could leverage the deep understanding their customers had of pizza and focus all of their attention on convincing customers they'd rather have a pizza that happens to have a stuffed crust.

Oklahoma-based Mazzio's Pizza tends to push the envelope, regularly introducing innovative new offers that dramatically alter the traditional pizza offer. One of their most recent innovations is the Quesapizza®, which combines aspects of a pizza with a quesadilla. Mazzio's has registered the name of their new creation as a trademark so that competitors can't quickly duplicate their offer. However, the company also has to work harder to educate customers on what a quesapizza is and why they might like it more than traditional pizzas offered by competitors.

In the technology marketing vernacular, quesapizza is a new product category and Mazzio's is a category maker. Stuffed crust pizza is a "me-too-plus" offer—it too is pizza but it has something that sets it apart.

What's the right answer for you? Now that you have mobilized your offer, should you position it as a new category or as a me-too-plus offer?

The right answer depends on a number of factors.

At its most basic level, the decision should be based on what best serves you and your customers. Will your customers best be able to decide whether or not to buy your new offer by starting from an understanding of an existing category and simply understand how you have improved it? Or will forcing your offer into an existing category misserve your customers because they will associate characteristics to your product (from that category) that are inappropriate and inaccurate, leading them to make a wrong decision? Neither you nor your customer are well served when they buy your offer with wrong expectations, or when they fail to buy your offer because they do not understand what is true and valuable about your offer.[1]

However, category-making decisions are never that simple. There are three fundamental factors that can impact your decision.

Perhaps the most critical factor is your current market position. If you are the market leader in an existing category, then you likely will be best served continuing in your existing category. For a new category to be successful, it has to be positioned against the existing category, proving to the customer how the "old way" has been devalued by new innovations. In other words, launching a new category devalues the category in which you are already the leader, undoing years of previous investments. In many cases, market leaders will be tempted to position their innovation as me-too-plus, even though it truly is a new category.

Challengers face the opposite temptation, seeing every innovation as a new category, even when customers will be better served by understanding the innovation as an incremental improvement to an existing category.

The second factor is defensibility. Market challengers who try to create a new category without considering how difficult it will be for the market leaders to convince customers that they can add the new capabilities to their existing offers are setting themselves up for a nasty fall.

TeleChoice, a strategic consultancy that has helped several companies create new categories in telecom and networking, cites the need for defensibility at an architectural level. If the current market leader can duplicate enough of the new advantage without having to change their technical or operational architecture, then challengers who attempt to make a category around this innovation are at particularly high risk.[2]

Danny Briere, CEO of TeleChoice, recalls Ipsilon as an example of a company that unadvisedly attempted to make a new category at the beginning of the Internet era. Ipsilon introduced a concept known as IP switching as a distinct category with order of magnitude performance improvement over the IP router category dominated by Cisco Systems.

"Ipsilon was the hottest game in town, for exactly six months," remembers Danny. "Then Cisco announced tag switching as a way to accomplish the same gains within the existing routing category. At that point, the game was up for Ipsilon."

For a new category to succeed, the category maker must have confidence that existing market leaders cannot or will not follow for several years given their technical and business constraints.

Within two years, Ipsilon was put out of its misery, acquired by Nokia for a fraction of its previous estimated value.

The third factor is budget. Convincing customers to take a risk on a new category is hard and expensive.

The decision to go with a new category offer is more involved for customers than simply comparing among the best alternatives in an existing category. Customers must understand what is wrong with the existing category and what is essential about the new category. They must become convinced that the dimension of improvement represented by the new category is important to them.

The decision to go with a new category is also dramatically higher risk for customers. For starters, new categories are unproven, and if they are well positioned, they involve an entirely new architecture for solving a problem that has been solved differently for years. Layer on the fact that categories are most often created by unproven market competitors, and the risk is amplified. Given that, by definition, a new category starts with only one provider, a customer betting on a new category cannot switch providers if there are problems with their first supplier.

To overcome these barriers, the category maker has to invest substantially in evangelism—preaching the good news of the new category and trying to win converts. This requires marketing and publicity expenditures well above what is required in introducing a new product in an existing category.

Is it worth it? If done well, category making can dramatically launch a company into the upper echelons of their industry. An example that Briere cites is TiVo.

TiVo defined a new way to watch television by introducing the digital video recorder (DVR) category. DVRs were positioned against VCRs, but offered order of magnitude improvements in usability and storage capacity. VCR manufacturers couldn't match TiVo's benefits with their existing architecture. TiVo became a huge success, rapidly establishing brand recognition, market share, and customer loyalty rarely matched by start-up companies.

However, the same results can be achieved by successfully marketing your new value in an existing category. Briere contrasts the success of Juniper Networks with the failure of Ipsilon. In the same year that Ipsilon failed to make a new category against Cisco Systems in IP switching, Juniper successfully launched products in the core routing category that Cisco had created and dominated. Juniper's innovations delivered meaningful incremental improvements along the performance dimensions that Cisco had defined for the category.

Within four years, Juniper had taken 30% market share away from Cisco. The two companies owned the market, accounting for 98% of all sales.[3] If you choose not to create a new category, then the challenges are different, but no less daunting. Standing out in a mature market where the rules of competition have been defined by powerful incumbents is never easy. Even in an existing category, customers must be convinced that the new value created through mobility is meaningful to them. This too requires investments in marketing and publicity.

Deliver the Value, Capture the Power

Whether or not you choose to position your mobilized product or service as a new category, communicating the benefits of mobility will be essential to translating the value you're creating for customers into power for your company in the competitive market.

All the work you have done up to this point should flow naturally into a launch plan. You have evaluated the ways in which mobility creates new value for customers. You have identified the best target customers and applications. You have put in place appropriate safeguards and you are ready to learn as your customers find new ways to derive value from mobility.

As you take your mobilized offer public, you may consider new ways to maximize your impact in the market. Should you develop a new vocabulary to create immediate traction around the value unleashed through mobility? Can you handpick some optimal customers who are willing to serve as case studies to clearly communicate how mobilization is creating tremendous new value? Can you participate in some high-profile events that will attract media and customer attention and that are particularly well suited to a mobilized offer? Can you convince a leading industry association or publication to add the value of mobility to the criteria they use in evaluating products and services for awards they issue each year, or perhaps to create a whole new award category?

At the end of the day, you need to execute flawlessly to truly deliver the power of mobility to your customers, but you must also create a market awareness of the value of mobility to make your investment pay off.

When the dust settles, and the rest of your industry wakes up to the fact that a technology revolution has once again redefined the rules of competition, will you be the one who has first grabbed hold of mobility and set the new rules? Having completed this book, I believe you will!

 FROM THE REAL WORLD

The Equilibrium of the Marketplace

In the preface to this book, I introduced the concept of a ten-layer stack that drives technology decisions, at least within communications networks. I presented the argument that the seven layers codified by technology standards as the OSI seven-layer model really only matter within the context of three additional layers: marketing, finance, and politics.

Whether any given technology truly matters to customers, ultimately gets adopted, and therefore has the opportunity to impact business and society rests in which of these three layers or forces has the greatest impact on decisions being made in the marketplace. I refer to this as the *equilibrium of the marketplace*.

The status quo has tremendous power in society and in business. Newton's first law—that a body at rest tends to stay at rest—is true in much more than just the science of physics. This truth is captured in many wise sayings, including "Let sleeping dogs lie" and "If it ain't broke, don't fix it." All of this truth and wisdom represents inertia that impedes the adoption and success of new technologies.

Marketing comes into play by communicating the value of the new technology in addressing the "latent desires" of the target market. People want things to be different, but they assume that their desires cannot be met, so they do not even bother asking. And realistically, their desires *can't* be met, until a technological breakthrough enables it. The role of marketing is to make people aware that the previous barriers have been broken and to awaken within them the desire for this capability.

This is a powerful force. Unchecked, even the smallest, simplest desire that could be met by new technology would overcome the marketplace inertia and would be immediately adopted. But neither society nor business is a frictionless world. There are largely unseen forces that impede this adoption and that must be overwhelmed if the technology is to disrupt the equilibrium and move the market.

The most powerful of these forces is politics. Continuing our Newtonian analogy, politics acts very much like friction. The force is virtually unnoticed until there's an attempt to move, and the force appears stronger as the force attempting to move the market increases.

The reality behind this is that those in control have much power and are generally happy with the status quo. Their power lies in the fact that they often have the most money, the most influence, and the most control over what people hear. They can out-shout, out-influence, and out-buy any attempt by challengers to disrupt the equilibrium of the marketplace.

As you can imagine, a new technology has to unleash powerful desires to overcome the incredible force of politics.

The third force, finance, is often the swing vote. Often, early in the life of a new technology, finance votes against adoption. But as the technology matures, finance can shift its vote, creating enough additional force for the desires unleashed by marketing to overcome the friction of politics and to upset the equilibrium in the marketplace.

Finance has three basic variables that come into play. The first is capital. How much does it cost to adopt the new technology? The second is operational expense. How does adopting the new technology change how much we will spend in the future—does it increase or decrease our need to spend? The third is revenue. Does the new technology enable me to make more money? These three variables are dispassionate, unlike the desires often unleashed by marketing and the power wielded by politics, but they can play the deciding factor in the minds of either consumer or business customers.

Early in the life of a new technology, the capital costs may be high and the operational expenses may be increased by the use of the technology. Potential new income from adoption of the new technology may be unproven. However, fine-tuning of the technology and the ability to share up-front costs over an increasing base of customers can reduce the capital and operating expenses, shifting the balance in favor of adoption, even as growth opportunities become clearer.

FROM THE REAL WORLD (CONTINUED)

In the end, these forces all play against each other, as shown in Exhibit 13.1. Either the status quo survives and the new technology disappears into oblivion or the desires of the marketplace and the economic advantages of the new technology overcome the political resistance of the ruling parties and the new technology emerges to disrupt society and business.

EXHIBIT 13.1

Powers Determining Adoption of New Technology

Latent Desires

| Capital | Expense | New Technology | New Revenue |

The Power of Rulers

Notes

1. TeleChoice. 2002. "Category Making in a Down Market," white paper, March 19.
2. Ibid.
3. Moritz, Scott. 2000. "Juniper Snatching Router Market Share From Cisco," November 22, www.thestreet.com/tech/networking/1184179.html.

Index

Index